# A CONTINUAL
# REMEMBRANCE

Letters from Sir William Osler
to his friend Ned Milburn
1865-1919

**SIR WILLIAM OSLER**
1849-1919

The original snapshot, made in the garden at Johns Hopkins in 1913, was given to Dr. Harvey Cushing by Dr. Lawrence Reynolds for the former's biography. Cushing's letter of thanks, written October 23, 1922, comments, "Most of his pictures have a very dour expression, which is missing in this one." (Cushing, Harvey: *Life of Sir William Osler*, Vol. II. Oxford, Clarendon Press, 1925, p. 352.)

# A CONTINUAL REMEMBRANCE

Letters from Sir William Osler
to his friend Ned Milburn
1865-1919

*By*

**HOWARD L. HOLLEY, B.S., M.D.**
*Professor of Medicine*
*Director Division of Rheumatology*
*University of Alabama in Birmingham*
*The Medical Center*
*Birmingham, Alabama*

*With a Foreword by*

**John W. Scott, M.A., M.D.**
*Bond Head, Ontario*

**CHARLES C THOMAS** • **PUBLISHER**
*Springfield* • *Illinois* • *U.S.A.*

*Published and Distributed Throughout the World by*
CHARLES C THOMAS • PUBLISHER
BANNERSTONE HOUSE
301-327 East Lawrence Avenue, Springfield, Illinois, U.S.A.
NATCHEZ PLANTATION HOUSE
735 North Atlantic Boulevard, Fort Lauderdale, Florida, U.S.A.

*With* THOMAS BOOKS *careful attention is given to all details of manufacturing and design. It is the Publisher's desire to present books that are satisfactory as to their physical qualities and artistic possibilities and appropriate for their particular use.* THOMAS BOOKS *will be true to those laws of quality that assure a good name and good will.*

*Printed in the United States of America*
*N-1*

*This book is dedicated to the memory of Lawrence Reynolds, M.D., whose great admiration for Sir William Osler was responsible for the acquisition of the letters in this volume and whose wish it was that they be edited for publication.*

*In the continual remembrance of a glorious past, individuals and nations find their noblest inspirations.*

---

*"The Leaven of Science," William Osler's address at dedication of Wistar Institute of Anatomy and Biology at the University of Pennsylvania, Philadelphia, May 21, 1894.

*The only way to have a friend is to be one.*

EMERSON

# Foreword

The Philistines will scoff at the appearance of yet another volume of Osleriana. However, these letters are, in a sense, the very essence of Osler's greatness. This did not lie in what he taught or how he taught it but rather in his ability to inspire trust, establish friendships and encourage others to excell themselves. To Osler friendships were sacred things, which must be cultivated and nourished. For like the talents, if they lie buried they produce nothing, but if utilized to the full, are highly productive.

In 1837 the Reverend Featherstone Osler arrived with his bride in a pioneer parish in the back-woods of Upper Canada. At that time less than half the land had been taken by settlers, and of this, very little was cleared. The roads, which appeared as straight lines on the surveyors plans, were merely forest trails, that meandered to avoid steep hills and swamps. A wrong turn could take the traveller miles out of his way, if he were not completely lost. In this setting, the value of friends and the need for neighbours was indelibly impressed upon the settlers mind.

Twelve years later, when William was born, the pioneer period had passed, yet many of the worthwhile customs and traditions survived. William's early training instilled in him the importance of other people and the appreciation of their feelings, hopes and sorrows. He carried this true sense of sympathy with him throughout his life. It formed an important ingredient of the *Art of Medicine* that he used so effectively throughout his professional career.

In these letters to Ned Milburn the development of a life-long friendship can be traced from an exuberent schoolboy companionship to a mature mutually supporting and satisfying relationship.

They show a facet of Osler's life that cannot be displayed in a formal biography, yet forms an essential part of his personality.

*Bond Head, Ontario*                        JOHN W. SCOTT, M.A., M.D.

# Preface

William Osler was without question the most prominent "man of medicine" in the late nineteenth and early twentieth centuries. His influence on the practice of medicine and on medical education was monumental and still endures. Indeed, he can be considered the progenitor of the present-day methods of teaching medical students. His idea that education "is a lifelong process" has been proven over and over again, while his human qualities of kindliness and unselfishness are as real today as they were over half a century ago.

Osler's rare gift of continuing friendship to all he chanced to meet has been unsurpassed. He had the grace of sympathy and the gleam of imagination with the ability to impart them to others. Osler believed, as did Montaigne, that "Friendship is nourished by communication," and he was a man who kept "his friendships in repair." Osler carried on a voluminous correspondence, always finding time to write letters, even during the busiest times of his eventful life. These letters reveal glimpses of a remarkable personality, matchless in depth of human interest and concern. Even during the last days of his life, when he was too ill to write for himself, he "would instruct his close friend and physician, Dr. Malloch, to write in his stead to those who would be expecting some message from him — old friends like Milburn, Ogden, and Shepherd."[1] Ned Milburn was his friend, and Osler was interested in all he said and did. The spark of their friendship through more than half a century was kept kindled by their continuing exchange of letters.

The letters published in this volume portray the warm, poignantly human story of a lifelong friendship between Sir William Osler and Edward (Ned) G. Milburn. This friendship

---

[1]Cushing, Harvey.: *Life of Sir William Osler*. Oxford, Clarendon Press, 1925. (Afterward referred to as "Cushing.")

began when they were teen-age classmates at a private school, and continued while they were together briefly in college. It was maintained throughout the more than fifty remaining years of their lives spent in separate countries and in different careers. While Sir William went on to become internationally famous as physician, teacher, and a scholar, Ned remained in Canada to become a teacher in the local school at Belleville, Ontario.

A half century of correspondence would reveal much of Osler personally, intellectually and spiritually. Unfortunately, his letters to Ned Milburn during the early period of his professional career were lost, probably thrown away by an industrious maid who had no way of knowing their subsequent value. The letters included in this volume reveal only the early and later years of Sir William's life. The early letters show clearly Osler's boyhood with all the exuberance of an irrepressible teen-age boy. This "normal" boyhood helped forge the depth of understanding and personality which gave him such exceptional insight in his relationships with his associates and students. Truly, in the enthusiastic reports of the young schoolboy and in the kind and thoughtful letters of the mature man can be sensed the immense vitality and unbounded mind of a man who demonstrated a concern in everyone and everything around him.

Osler, in spite of being brought up in a parsonage, was not a "good" little boy. Indeed, he was quite a mischief-maker, whose pranks sometimes resulted in disastrous consequences to the recipient. Though somewhat subdued by time, this characteristic remained with him all of his life, and his whimsical humor together with his skill as a raconteur delighted everyone he met. It was this characteristic gaity and humanness that contributed the most outstanding qualities of his personality, deep understanding and great human kindness toward his fellow man. His humility in a world full of praise for his accomplishments was inspiring, for the grace of humility is truly the measure of a man's greatness.

# Introduction

Two boys, William Osler and Ned Milburn, were products of pioneer life in Canada. Their childhood was spent in that Dominion during the time of its continuing settlement and early development. Although more of Osler's early years were spent in the frontier wilderness, Milburn also experienced the invigorating impact of this era. These formative years gave to the two youths great strength, self-reliance, curiosity, and the ability to create their own entertainment (often to the dismay of their elders). They learned particularly the meaning of hard work, and the stage was set for development of characters which were destined to influence all with whom they would come in contact.

William Osler, born July 12th, 1849, was the eighth child of Ellen Pickton and the Reverend Mr. Featherstone Lake Osler. Reverend Mr. Featherstone Osler, an ordained minister of the Church of England, had chosen to enter the mission field and had come from England in 1837 to establish a church on the edge of the Canadian wilderness at Bond Head near Lake Simcoe, in Ontario.

William received his early education at home, mostly under the tutelage of his mother. His later excellence as a student of the Bible can be attributed to his Christian training as a lad. A school was eventually established at Bond Head, and the Osler children attended it for several years. However, the Oslers deemed further education of utmost importance for their offspring. This was in part the reason for their move to the town of Dundas, Ontario, where they sent their children to a well-known local school. Later, they arranged for the boys to go to boarding school at Barrie. William also attended a college preparatory school at Weston.

It was while in school at Weston that William Osler first became interested in the natural sciences. The Reverend Mr. W. A. Johnson, warden and founder of Trinity College Grammar School at Weston, introduced him to the wonderful world of science. Johnson was an expert botanist and microscopist and possessed the gift for inspiring his students.

It was also at Weston that Osler became acquainted with Dr. James Bovell of Toronto, a good friend and frequent visitor in the home of the Reverend Mr. Johnson. Dr. Bovell was a physician, educator, and a naturalist of great brilliance. Osler, together with Reverend Mr. Johnson's son, was enlisted to assist Dr. Bovell in his periodic forays for zoological specimens.

Despite Osler's early spirited ways, he was apparently inclined to study for the ministry and was sent to Trinity College in Toronto for this purpose. However, after one term there, Osler summarily announced that he was leaving Trinity to attend medical school. He entered the Toronto School of Medicine in October 1868. Dr. Bovell was delighted, and Osler was invited to live in his home. In return for this privilege, the young student assisted the doctor in keeping his patient appointments and aided him in his scientific studies. Osler had maintained a close association with Dr. Bovell during his stay at Trinity College, and he often attended Bovell's lectures at the Toronto School of Medicine. It is certain that this new experience had a profound and far-reaching effect on young Osler, as later in life he remarked that his year at Trinity College (1867-68) convinced him that medicine would be his chosen field. He is quoted as saying that it was his relationship with Bovell which made him realize the truth of that phrase in the Hippocratic oath which states

I will honour as my father the man who teaches me the art.

In 1870, on the advice of Dr. Bovell, he entered McGill University at Montreal in order to continue his medical education.

William Osler's first introduction to great literature also came during his stay in Toronto. While living at the home of Dr. Bovell, Osler had free access to Bovell's personal library, which happily was filled with a choice and varied collection of books. The long winter evenings gave him ample time to acquaint himself with the minds of the world's great men of wisdom. Osler afterwards stated that it was this stimulating experience that aroused in him an enduring interest in books. It was probably during this time that he began reading for half an hour in bed before sleeping, a custom that became a habit of a lifetime. Indeed, he became so interested in classical literature that his mastery of the art of letters has made his literary contributions as much a part of his heritage as that of his scientific accomplishments.

Apparently Osler had a penchant for seeking out and cultivating the friendship of men of letters and learning. During the summer of 1871, while in school in Montreal, he became acquainted with Dr. Palmer Howard, Professor of Medicine at McGill, who also put his library at Osler's disposal. Osler later said of Palmer Howard that he was an ideal teacher, studious, energetic, and enthusiastic, and that he had "never known one in whom was more happily combined a stern sense of duty with the mental freshness of youth."

Years later, Osler paid tribute to his mentors, the Reverend Mr. W. A. Johnson, James Bovell, and Robert Palmer Howard, when he said it was to these three men that he owed his success in life ". . . if success means getting what you want and being satisfied with it." However, of the three, it was Dr. Howard who gained Osler's greatest and most enduring respect and gratitude.

After Osler graduated from McGill University in 1872, he spent a year visiting the medical centers in Europe and worked during the winter at the Physiological Laboratory at University College, London. In 1874, after London and the continent, he returned to Canada with a fine store of knowledge but no money and few prospects for the future. For several weeks he relieved the local practitioner in Dundas, after which he worked with Dr. Charles O'Reilly who was the Resident Physician at the City Hospital in Hamilton, Ontario. In 1875 Dr. O'Reilly was appointed as the medical superintendent to the Toronto General Hospital, a post from which he retired in 1905.

In July 1874, Palmer Howard, Professor of Medicine at McGill, wrote Osler a letter offering him a position as lecturer in pathology and physiology at McGill University, which he promptly accepted.

He went to Montreal in August 1874 where his enthusiasm and industry became a byword among his colleagues. The use of the microscope, teaching in the wards, the writing of scientific papers — everything occupied him except private patients, for whom he had neither the time nor the inclination. "He lived frugally — undisturbed by poverty." A year later he was made a full professor on the faculty. For the next ten years while at Mc-Gill, Osler did some of his most outstanding original scientific work. He also became widely acclaimed as a clinician.

In June 1884, he resigned his position at McGill to accept the professorship of clinical medicine at the University of Pennsylvania. His appearance at Philadelphia has been described as "a breath of fresh air let into a stifling room." It was here that he was able to apply his unconventional approach to the teaching of medicine. In this he insisted that teaching be done at the bedside rather than in the lecture room. Osler had the unique ability to inspire the student to seek further knowledge by experiment, by reading, and by enjoying the history of the subject. He was a masterful teacher who could create interest in his pupils by the magnetism of his own enthusiasm.

In May 1889 he accepted an appointment as physician-in-chief at the newly organized Johns Hopkins Hospital in Baltimore, Maryland. He found there the freedom that he needed to develop a truly great teaching service. There he married Grace Revere Gross, the widow of his friend, Dr. Samuel Gross, of Philadelphia. There also were born his two sons, the first of whom died a week after birth. His textbook *Principles and Practice of Medicine* was finished. It was at Johns Hopkins that Osler had the stimulation of close association with such men of other medical disciplines as Halsted, Welch, and Kelly. Truly, he had reached the zenith of a remarkable career.

In 1905, he left Hopkins to become Regius Professor of Medicine at Oxford. With his leaving, Hopkins had literally "lost its soul." At Oxford he hoped to find the leisure to write and read his beloved books. Such was not to be the case, as he soon became engrossed in many of the health problems of his adopted country. With deepest anguish, he saw England through a great World War, 1914–18, in which his only son was killed in action. Though crushed by sorrow he continued his work both in medicine and in great literature until 1919, when he became ill. William Osler died on the 29th of December of that year.

Osler's intellect, character, and spirit of charity inspired and influenced every life that he touched. His enthusiasm was contagious, and his capacity for continuing friendship was unique. He kept in touch with a host of friends throughout his life, if only with brief notes, often scribbled on postal cards, but his friendship for Ned Milburn occupied a notable place in his life. His high regard and love for this friend is reflected not only in his lifelong correspondence, but also in so many acts of thoughtful concern to Ned and the members of his family.

Edward (Ned) Fairfax Milburn was born April 13th, 1849, the youngest of ten children. His early life was as happy as that of William Osler's for Milburn enjoyed a small-town life and a prosperous father. Joseph Milburn, Ned's father, emigrated to Canada in 1819 from Northumberland, England. Shortly afterwards, he married Desdemona Post, the daughter of a York (now Toronto) watchmaker. They operated a tavern and a farm. The eldest sons were apprentice workers in a nearby tannery.

The lives of the two boys, William Osler and Ned Milburn, were inevitably associated with the early history of Canada. The first government of the colony was patterned after that of England, with a Governor General appointed by the King. The parliament was made up of a lower house, whose members were elected by the people, but its voice in the government was extremely limited. The members of the upper house were appointed for a life term by the Governor General. From this was selected a Legislative-Executive Council which exercised considerable control of the government in making appointments, not only to national but also to local offices. This small central party was known as the "Family Compact" and it kept the reins of government firmly in its hands. However, on November 25th, 1837, William Lyon MacKenzie proclaimed a new government in Upper Canada and on December 7th organized a force of eight-hundred to nine-hundred rebels near Toronto. They were soon routed by the regular troops and MacKenzie fled to the United States where the

U. S. authorities permitted him to continue his harassment of the government of Upper Canada.

The Reverend Mr. Featherstone Osler resigned his commission in the British Navy in 1833. He arrived in Canada in July, 1837, with no knowledge of local politics but took a strong dislike to Archdeacon (later Bishop) John Strachan, one of the members of the "Family Compact." Having been a naval officer, he had no patience with armed rebellion, but later as he came to know the "Family Compact" better he lost sympathy with them.

Joseph Milburn* joined MacKenzie's Patriots in 1837 in their fight against the oligarchy of the "Family Compact." Because he was a Quaker, he did not actually fight in the rebellion. Nevertheless, he was arrested for "high treason" and spent eight months in the York gaol awaiting trial. He was sentenced to be transported to Van Dieman's Land (now Tasmania) but was one of those pardoned by Queen Victoria in celebration of her coronation.

In 1864, Willie Osler met Ned Milburn at Barrie Grammar School, where both had been sent to school. Whether it was their mutual love of fun which drew them together is not known, nor for that matter is much known of Ned Milburn's disposition. However, there is ample evidence that Willie Osler was already well versed in the way of mischief-making, and even at this early date Osler demonstrated qualities of leadership, albeit devilment-bent, which attracted other boys. The friendship between the two school boys which began in the fall of 1886 was to be a lasting one.

The following spring Ned was sent to a school in Georgetown, while Osler remained at Barrie for another term. It was during this time that the correspondence between the two boys began, a correspondence which was to last until the death of Sir William in 1919. These letters from Osler to Milburn are the ones published in this volume.

Osler went to Trinity College Grammar School at Weston in January 1866, while Ned entered Trinity College in Toronto the following fall. In the autumn of 1867, Osler entered Trinity College also, and the good friends were together again. The boys,

*He changed the spelling of his name after coming to Canada.

now young men, were perhaps busier with their studies than they had been previously, for there is little mention of activities shared. Probably there was no need for writing, as they could see each other frequently.

Milburn received his B.A. degree from Trinity College in December 1869, then moved to the town of Belleville, Ontario, where he lived the remainder of his life. In 1887, he married Isabella Benjamin, daughter of a member of the Canadian Parliament, who had come to Upper Canada in its early years to start a conservative newspaper. Ned and Isabella had four children, three daughters and a son, Edward George Joseph, who died in 1904, when he was twenty-four years old.

The years brought rewards to the Milburns — happy days sailing in the boat that Ned had built, singing in the church choir (for he had a fine baritone voice) and teaching in the local school. He was principal of Belleville High School from 1894 until 1908, when he retired to teach again. As an adult he was a reserved man, stern but just. The Tory had replaced the prankster. His pupils respected and admired him, often visiting him long after their graduation. He died on his seventy-sixth birthday, April 13th, 1926.

When Osler visited Canada, and occasion permitted, he went to see Milburn at Belleville, or if time would not permit, he would send him the railroad fare in order that they might visit together in Toronto. Although Milburn and Osler saw each other only infrequently after the years at Trinity College, their close friendship continued through their correspondence. His last letter to Ned Milburn was written only a month before Osler's death.

When Dr. Harvey Cushing was preparing to write his biography of William Osler, he solicited Edward Milburn's aid, and it was to Milburn that Lady Osler presented the first copy of Cushing's life of Osler. In one of the letters to Cushing from Milburn, he pays eloquent tribute to Osler, his friend of a lifetime, stating that his personal magnetism seemed to increase with age. "People who met him for the first time have told me that after a few minutes' talk with him, they felt that they had known him for years. He had all the best qualities of a manly man like

Corin.[1] He owed no man hate, glad of other man's good, content with his own harm, ambitious for others, never for himself. He loved much and his love was returned by multitudes. His was a life of service to humanity, and like the Man of Nazareth, went about doing good and healing all manner of sickness and disease among the people."

---

[1]A shepherd, in Shakespeare's *As You Like It*.

# Acknowledgments

Sometimes titles are written for books after the book has been completed, and with great effort to find the appropriate one; but before even starting this book, and after only brief digging into the life of Sir William Osler, the title of this book of his edited letters to Ned Milburn just seemed to leap from Osler's own words.

For the permission to use the letters published in this volume I am deeply indebted to the Lawrence Reynolds Historical Library in the University of Alabama in Birmingham, Medical Center. The letters are a part of a magnificent collection of medical historical material bequeathed to the University by the late Dr. Lawrence Reynolds of Detroit, Michigan and Ozark, Alabama.

My very special thanks go to the Medical Center for providing the time away from my duties there, without which it would have been impossible to write this volume.

Invaluable assistance has been rendered me by Mrs. Martha Lou Thomas, Custodian of the Reynolds Historical Collection. She has acted as research assistant and critic throughout the preparation of this manuscript. I am also most grateful to Mrs. Sarah Brown, Librarian of the Medical Center, for her kindness and encouragement during the compilation of the manuscript.

I would like to express my appreciation to Mr. Barry O'Dwyer of McGill University for the historical research into the early beginnings of both the Osler and Milburn families, and for the cooperation shown me by Miss Cécile Desbarats, Librarian, and Mrs. P. F. O'Dwyer, Cataloguer of the Osler Library, McGill University, Montreal, P.Q., Canada.

Dr. Gene V. Ball and Dr. Robert S. Hogan graciously edited a portion of the manuscript. To Dr. Walter B. Frommeyer, Jr., a special note of appreciation for his aid and encouragement in my work. My thanks to Dr. John Scott, of the University of Toronto, for his criticism and for the excellent "Foreword" he has contributed to this book.

I am indebted to Mrs. Lois T. Montgomery for deciphering my handwriting and for the typing of the manuscript. Without her assistance and patience my job would have been much more difficult. I owe a most particular thank you to Miss Geneva Blackburn for painstakingly checking each letter published herein. To Mrs. Irene Harper, who typed the manuscript for publication, goes praise for an onerous task well done.

This book was not written without a great deal of help from others, and it is my fear that I may fail in my acknowledgments for the assistance which was given me by so many people, not only those here in Birmingham, but also the ones in Canada and Baltimore.

Above all, I am grateful to my wife for her devoted labor in editing and her astute criticism of the text, and most of all for her remarkable and enduring patience. She has been a research assistant, cartographer, and editor through every stage of the preparation of the story. She deserves more credit than I can give and still list myself the author.

H. L. H.

# Contents

# A CONTINUAL REMEMBRANCE

Letters from Sir William Osler
to his friend Ned Milburn
1865-1919

FIGURE 1. Old church and rectory at Bond Head. From Osler Collection, Academy of Medicine, Toronto.

# I
# The Early Years

*I started life in the best of all environments — in a parsonage, one of nine children.*\*

William Osler spent the first eight years of his life at Bond Head, on the edge of the great Canadian wilderness, where conditions were ideal for the development of a young boy, both in physical growth and moral character.

The duties of Featherstone Osler's ministerial office required him to be away from home often, and for the most part the Osler boys had full responsibility for the essential chores. In their primitive surroundings, heat, food, and shelter were the products of their own labor, and consequently the jobs to be done were many and varied. From necessity, they learned to work as a team, which undoubtedly served them in good stead later in life.

The Oslers were not rigid disciplinarians. In fact, Featherstone was rather indulgent, and although Ellen held the reins of discipline firmly, she rarely applied a check without an absolute need. Although they "spared the rod" the children were regularly exposed to a "goodly supply of religious training."

They were a hardy lot — from the very beginning, the Osler boys were rugged tartars; their uncle once wrote he hoped they would "improve with age." Certainly they were a menace to at least one neighbor, who refused to allow her children to begin the short journey to the local school in Bond Head until the "Osler troupe" had passed her home.

William had early training in the art of mischievousness and deviltry, but underneath this facade he was a bright and unusually industrious boy. Even as a lad he often showed his unselfish and affectionate nature. He was quick to share the last penny of his scant pocket money, even though the Oslers were far from affluent.

---

\*Osler, W.: *A Way of Life*. London, Constable and Co., 1913.

One of the earliest escapades that has been recorded occurred when William was five years old. It occurred while he was cutting wood for the stove and Charlotte (the "Chattie" of his later letters), his seven-year-old sister, attempted to tease him by putting her finger repeatedly on the spot he was about to strike with his hatchet. Finally William, in exasperation, said, "I will count to three and if you don't take it off I will chop it off." And chop it off he did![1]

The Oslers became increasingly concerned about the education of their children. The school facilities in Bond Head were considerably limited. In 1854, Featherstone Osler felt impelled to write Bishop Strachan of Toronto to request that he be transferred, partly on the basis of his health, which probably had been adversely affected by the necessity of constant travel in all types of weather, but more particularly because of the pressing need for the children's education. As a result, Canon Osler was assigned to Dundas, Ontario.

---

[1]Cushing, vol. I, p. 18.

FIGURE 2A. Rectory at Dundas. Published in *Osler Memorial Number,* Bull. No. IX, International Association of Medical Museums, Abbott, M. E. (Ed.) , Montreal.

FIGURE 2B. Home of the Joseph Milburns, Ned's parents, Oakville, Ontario, circa 1870. (Courtesy of Miss Ruby Milburn.)

# II

# Dundas

*Chattie, I've got the sack.**

After the move from Bond Head (Tecumseth Province) to Dundas, the Osler children became well known around the village, where they were dubbed "Tecumseth Cabbage," probably reflecting their rural origin, but the "cabbage" soon became a favorite vegetable to the town's young fry. They fitted easily into any situation which arose and so insured continued popularity. Many tales of William's school days have survived. Some he told himself to amuse the younger generation; others were remembered and related by his school chums.

While in Dundas, William attended the local grammar school, which had an excellent reputation. The school, unfortunately, shared the building with a common school which had quarters on the ground floor, while the grammar school was upstairs. Evidently a state of continuous war existed between the two groups of pupils. William soon became the leader of the grammar school troupe, and he was eventually expelled from the school in 1864. No one is certain just what particular incident caused his dismissal, but it most likely was the result of an accumulation of grievances due to his many escapades. It may have been the noisy flock of geese that greeted the principal[1] of the common school when he unlocked the school one Monday morning; or perhaps his patience came to an end when he found the desks and benches had been removed from his classroom. Someone had painstakingly unscrewed them from the floor and they were eventually dis

---

*Cushing, vol. I, p. 22.

[1]"Doubtless, Mr. Flynn, the principal, was the victim of many pranks on the part of his own irrepressible pupils, of whom there was probably none more notorious than a rollicking boy named Willie Osler, who, though adored by all, was particularly ingenious in evolving and perpetrating practical jokes of an elaborate and unusual sort, in which, as a rule, he took the leadership." Cushing, vol. I, p. 22

covered stored in the attic, to which the only means of access was a stepladder and trapdoor.

Another version of the dismissal was that William and nine other boys caught the schoolmaster using a Latin "crib" and shouted epithets of their disapproval through a keyhole; but whatever the culminating episode — expelled he was.* His parents maintained that the Methodists on the school board were responsible for William's dismissal. To them it did seem peculiar that the only pupil expelled was the son of the established English church clergyman. (Cushing relates that William was expelled along with four accomplices.) William was singularly unperturbed by his dismissal, for he galloped home and greeted his sister Chattie with a joyful shout, "I've got the sack."

After the fracas at Dundas Grammar School, his parents packed him off to the Barrie Garmmar School, where his three older brothers had been previously in school. But William's personality did not change merely with a change of scene. For the lovable mischief-maker from Dundas soon became the leader of a fun-loving group at this school.

---

*"That against your son was that he, when passing to the school, put his mouth to the keyhole of the door and called out contemptuously, 'Come out old McKee' and other disparaging terms." From the Dundas *True Banner*, June 2, 1864 (quoted in Cushing) .

FIGURE 3. Barrie school where Osler and Milburn first met in 1864. (From Cushing's *Life of Sir William Osler* (1925). Vol. I, p. 24.)

# III

# Osler Goes to Barrie School

*In my school days I was much more bent upon mischief than upon books.\**

At Barrie School there were about fourteen boys who were "boarders," and in addition there were those who lived at home in the town and attended the school. Apparently the relations between these two groups of students were at best strained. There were three of the boarders who quickly earned the appellation of "Barrie's Bad Boys," although one of them, Ned Milburn, hints that this terminology was mild in contrast to other names by which they were frequently known. They were Osler, Ned Milburn, and Charlie Locke. Osler, already well-schooled in making mischief, quickly assumed the leadership of this unholy trio. Mr. Milburn wrote Cushing[1] that "the spirit of fun was well marked in him (Osler), real fun that hurt nobody, but sometime caused a little annoyance to the victims of the joke." He also wrote somewhat sanctimoniously that "we were often blamed for the misdoings of ill-conditioned boys belonging to the town, even though we could prove a perfectly good alibi."

"Barrie's Bad Boys" were good at athletics as well as practical jokes. They excelled in cricket, racing, and other sports. There is a story told by Milburn of how he and Osler once attempted to swim across Kempenfeldt Bay accompanied by a boat. The icy waters forced Ned to give up the contest, but Willie continued all the way![2]

---

\**The Albany Medical Annals*, xx:307--309, June, 1899. Address to the students of the Albany Medical College, February 1, 1899.

[1]Cushing Archives, Yale University.

[2]Cushing, vol. I, p. 26.

Studies were not neglected. The boys would study diligently, especially just before exam time. When "lights out" was ordered at 9:30 P.M., they frequently climbed out the dormitory window, six feet above the ground, and read by the light of the moon, after which they would go for a refreshing swim in the Bay a few hundred yards from the school. All of these forbidden activities were unknown to the school authorities. Once, as told by Cushing, while on one of their periodic nocturnal forays, they discovered a man's clothes left on the bay shore by someone who was enjoying a late swim in the nude. The boys promptly secured them and would not return them until the swimmer, a prominent M.P. from the district, agreed to take the boys on a future boat ride. Obviously a part of the bargain was not to mention the incident to Mr. Checkley, head of the school. Good as his word, the story goes, the M.P. kept his part of the bargain.

On another occasion, when these three boys had been cam-pused for a week for robbing a neighbor's melon patch, Osler retaliated for this indignity by climbing upon the schoolhouse roof, where he covered the chimney with a board. Of course, the building soon became full of smoke, and the boys watched with ill-concealed glee while the Barrie Hook and Ladder Company came charging up to put out the nonexistent fire.[3]

It was with great delight that Osler used to retell the pranks of these Barrie School days to one of his special children friends.

> Sir William used to tell me stories of his boyhood as I sat on the floor at his knees by the library fire. . . . He would always laugh till the tears came into his eyes. . . . During those last sad years I never saw him laugh so heartily or look so happy as when he forgot the pres-ent and lived again his old pranks.
>
> DUNDAS[,][4] Jan. 10th [1865]

Dear Ned[5]

It was a cursed shame that we did not see each other when we were

---

[3]Cushing, vol. I, p. 25.

[4]Dundas is in Wentworth County, forty miles west of Toronto.

[5]Ned Milburn was no longer in school at Barrie. He probably left in December 1864 and was in Oakville when he received this letter, twenty-two miles southwest of Toronto. Ned and Willie were together at Barrie during the fall of 1863-64. Osler arrived a few months after Ned. Milburn and Osler were about fifteen and one-half years old at this time.

in Toronto[.] Jemmy and I looked all over for you but could not find you.[6] I have not gone back to school yet for I do not know whether Mr. Checkley is going to stay in Barrie or going to Toronto to take the Neber Gram School so I have [had] good long holidays[.][7] I suppose there will be no chance of my seeing you when I go down. Don't you write till you get another letter from me for you will not know where to direct it[.] I may be either in Toronto[.] Dundas or Barrie. Frank[8] is in Toronto yet doing nothing[.]

Believe me your affection [sic]

School chum<br>W Osler

This is the first letter that Osler wrote Milburn. It was probably written during the Christmas vacation while Osler was at his home in Dundas. Milburn had left Barrie to enter the school at Georgetown while Osler remained at the Barrie school.

The early letters of Osler to Milburn reveal how sorely "Willie" missed his school chum, and they also reflect even at this early date Osler's unusual propensity for friendship and his capacity for "a continual remembrance."

Francis, twin brother to Chattie and the sixth son born to Featherstone and Ellen Osler, was a typical "black sheep of the family." Closest to William in age, and most like him in looks and manner, Francis (Frank) Osler was an irresponsible individual, always in trouble. Throughout his life he never gave up this role. In school, however, Frank apparently participated actively in sports.

Frank left William at Trinity College Grammar School to follow the lure of the sea, much as his father had done in his

---

[6]Jemmy Morgan (James Chapin Morgan) lived in Barrie where his family was prominent in professional circles. In a letter to Cushing, Milburn wrote about Jemmy Morgan "when we were in Barrie, he was a fourth year student in the University of Toronto. We used to meet him in vacation times and became great friends." Morgan was a few years older than Osler and Milburn.

[7]Francis Checkley was master of the grammar school. He was a brother of Reverend W. F. Checkley, Inspector of Grammar Schools. 'Mr. Checkley took high honors in his University being a scholar of Trinity College, Dublin. He was mathematical master in the late Model Grammar School, and is now one of the Masters of Upper Canada College." From Barrie *Northern Advance*, Jan. 13, 1865.

[8]The letter refers to William Osler's brother Frank, who was then eighteen years of age and in school with Osler at Barrie.

youth. Later, he married Isabel Fowler, and tried to settle down in British Columbia as a fruit rancher. His elder brother, Edmund, a banker, gave them a regular allowance. The fact that he gave it into Belle's hands rather than Frank's speaks volumes of this man with William's merry spirit, but none of his "grit."

Osler wrote Ned again from his home in Dundas. Ned was at home in Oakville and planned to attend school in Georgetown in the fall. Osler in this letter referred to his pending admission to the school at Weston in September. It also alludes to the well-known athletic prowess of the two boys.

DUNDAS[,] July 13 [1865]

Dear Ned

I am almost ashamed to write to you as I ought to have written last week[,] but you know what a awfull [sic] bother writting [sic] is to boys[.] I heard from wild Irishman[9] this week and he says that Barrie is so dammed lonely now "that he will go clear up out of the land[.]" [He]says that Magge and Nelly and their unmentionables are all right.[10] I heard from Jemmy [and] he said that he was going to write to you soon. The govenor [sic] is not going to send me back to Barrie and Mr. Checkley reccommended [sic] Weston[11] and I think I am going there[.] Jemmy Morgan says it is a splendid place[,] but I do not much like the appearance of it on the map[,] it is 9 miles from Toronto. Mr. Johnson[12] the minister there is the head of the school but he does not teach. A Trinity coledge [sic] chap teaches. I believe there are a good many girls there[.] When you write tell me where you are going after the holidays. The governor [sic] found out Frank[13] [was] smoking and gave him the devil of a lecture but he did not care much as he was smoking a 1/4 of an hour afterwards. I have got my nephew on my knee and it is hard work writing with him jogging

[9]Charlie Locke, known as the "wild Irishman," was the third member of the trio known as "Barrie's Bad Boys." In later life he became a prominent physician in Montreal, but he died quite young. Osler aided his family in many ways. One son trained at Hopkins under Osler.

[10]In the Directory for Ontario, Canada, for 1871 is listed a Miss Maggie Morton, Milliner. Apparently this was the "Magge and Nelly" and their "unmentionables" to which Osler refers.

[11]Trinity College Grammar School, Weston. The Reverend Osler apparently changed his mind, as Osler went back to Barrie for the fall term, 1865.

[12]Reverend W. A. Johnson was founder of the Trinity College Grammar School at Weston and served as warden of the school until it was moved to Port Hope.

[13]Frank Osler.

the pen[.]14 There is not much doing down here[.] I have had a good deal of boating (I have just shipped that youngone of[f] my knee) [.] The blasted lunatics down here have got up baseball clubs all over the town from the young one 2 years old to old men[.] I belong to a club but I do not like it much[.] There are bushels of cherries and I feed sumptuously every day on them. There are going to be lots of peaches[.] I have only been on one drunk since I came home that was on the 5th at the Sunday School picnic and and had lots of fun with the girls.15 Mrs. Stuart and my sister went to Toronto this morning by the boat[.] Mrs. Stuart is beginning to swell about the stomach[.]

That accident that happened to young Coleman and his sister have [sic] scared all the people about boats and the man that builds boats has been doing very little business[.] I suppose you have plenty of boating[.]

[T]here was a heavy east storm on Monday[.] I was down to the lake that day but it was to[o] rough for me to venture out in the boat I had. I hope you will come to Weston if I do[.]

> I remain your affectionate
> friend and schoolmate
> W. Osler

DUNDAS[,] 1 Aug. [1865]

Dear Ned

I got your letter about ten days ago, and I see by it that you have been cutting it hard with the girls[.] I saw in the paper that the Oakville boys were beaten but I hope you will have better luck in the return match. We have played two matches since we came down both in Hamilton[.] We beat them once by 26 runs[.] Frank16 made the crack score (33) and in the return match last Saturday we were beaten by 1 run and 9 wickets to go down for our three best players were out of town. Last Friday Frank and I and another chap rowed down to Oakland17 to see Harry Leslie18 walk the tight rope which he did very well. [W]e were on the tight of course[.] [W]e had a hard row up as

---

14The nephew that was "jogging the pen" was probably Featherstone's son. Featherstone was Osler's older brother who later became a well known jurist in the Dominion.

15Osler was a teetotaler early in his life, so this apparently was intended as a joke.

16Frank Osler.

17Oakland was a waterfront suburb of the City of Hamilton, Ontario, located about five miles from Dundas.

18Harry Leslie, an American rope stunt artist, crossed the Niagara River on a tight rope while shackled with chains July 28, 1865. (The Hamilton [Ontario] Evening Times.)

there was a strong west wind and it was raining like the devil. The duck shooting begins on Wendsday [sic] and I am going to have my gun rigged up. There was a boy from Dundas down at Montreal and went to Mrs. Lay[19] and Bob is going to school in the states just what I said that he would be doing. The govenor [sic] got a letter from Mr. Johnson of Weston telling him that the school did not open till some time in September so I shall have had nearly 12 weeks holidays.[20] I have lots of fun now as the harvest apples are ripe and I can get a horse and boat whenever I like[.] I must finish off by saying that I walked home last night with a Car[r]ie Cathune[21] of Guelph who is staying at Tom Watts[.] I remain your affec. frien[d] and school chum

W. Osler

P.S. Frank began to write and after wasting 3 sheets of paper left off.

William was just 16 years of age and Milburn only a few months older. This letter again was written from William's home (the rectory) in Dundas where he went after the spring school term at Barrie was over. Contemporary writers have described the rectory in Dundas as a replica of an English manor house with both a wonderful fruit and flower garden. Summer, with its bounty of fruits, must have been a veritable paradise for the Osler children.

BARRIE[.] Oct. 17th [1865]

Dear Ned

It is a shame that I have not written to you before but I have been waiting for that Irishman for the last three weeks. He is just ahead of me [in school] writing like the devil[.] We have had good times lately with George Stuart (Hamilton Stuart[']s brother) [.][22] We went out sailing every evening [sic] in Mr. Brailes boat[.] [H]e has just got a six inch keel put on her and two sails and she goes like the devil, every time we go out we go to Meeking's and have two or three good horns in Meeking's parlor and Mr. Stuart get[s] at the piano and

---

[19]Mrs. Lay, principal of a young ladies' school in Montreal, 33 Beaver Hall Terrace.
[20]Reverend William A. Johnson.
[21]Osler was obviously trying to impress Ned on his relationship with girls. Carrie Carthune, to whom he referred, was about 13 years of age at this time.
[22]Lovell's Directory of Ontario 1871, under Barrie, lists Hamilton D. Stewart (Osler probably misspelled the name) as an attorney. George was probably a student at Barrie.

sings the dirtiest songs out of jail.[23] [H]e has quite demorilised [sic]
F. and J. Checkley[.][24] [H]e left on the 9th but is coming back next
summer. Jemmy Morgan left two weeks ago yesterday and I have not
heard from him since. We are getting on very well in our studies[.]
[W]e have finished the Manilian [sic] and are doing Horace and Pro
Archia Poeta and the fifth Book of Xenophen[.]

Maloy[25] got two scolarships [sic] at Queens Colledge [sic].

[T]here were two new chaps came yesterday[,] Chappel and Drury
from the country. We do nothing but play shinny and Charlie[26] and
I go down town and get into Jo Locke's room and smoke and eat
bullzies[.][27] I just looked over to Charlie and as he got such a long
letter I must wind up. With best love to you old chap, wishing you
were with us again in Barrie

> I remain your affection [sic]
> School chum
> Willie Osler

P[.]S[.] I quite forgot to tell you of our hooking apples scrapes at
Lally[']s[28] but Charlie will give you a full account, excuse this
damned bad writing as I have a bad pen

This letter was written after Osler had returned to Barrie for
the fall session of school. Ned had been sent to Georgetown to
school. Charlie Locke is probably the boy referred to in the letters
as the wild Irishman. The letter presaged Osler's future ability to
express himself in his writings and revealed the depth of affection
and tenacious loyalty in which he held his friend Ned.

---

[23]Meeking's Hotel, General Store and Auctioneering business, Barrie, Ontario.

[24]F. and J. Checkley, sons of the headmaster.

[25]Maloy, William, registered at Queen's University, Kingston, Ontario, in 1865, 1866,
and 1867.

[26]J. Charlie Locke.

[27]Jo Locke — storekeeper.

[28]Lally's — probably Edmund Lally, an agent for the Canadian Bank of Commerce
or Francis Lally, a barrister. Both were residents of Barrie.

# IV

## Osler Goes to Weston

*He possessed the genius of Friendship.**

In 1864, the Reverend William Arthur Johnson, rector of the Parish of Weston, applied to the Trinity College Corporation (Toronto) for permission to establish a college preparatory school at Weston to be known as "The Trinity College School."[1] The Reverend Johnson offered to provide the site or a building for the school's use out of private funds he had previously collected. This proposal received the support of the members of the faculty at Trinity College — notably Dr. James Bovell. Dr. Bovell became the medical director of the grammar school and spent most of his weekends there, much to the dismay of his private patients in Toronto. The school opened in 1865. The school at Barrie had been steadily declining in reputation, so when a new school was begun in Weston by Reverend William Johnson, it immediately

---

*J. G. Adami: *Memorial Number.* Bull. No. IX of the Inter Ass of Med Museums, M. E. Abbott, (Ed.), Montreal, 1927, p. 83.

[1]A similar school was likewise begun the same year at Picton, Ontario, under the auspices of the Bishop (Anglican) of Ontario. Immediately, competition and rivalry began between the two schools. There were several attempts made to combine the two schools. Meanwhile, at Weston friction developed due to the dual control of the school (Father Johnson was not headmaster; he was the warden, probably as a result of his differences with Bishop Strachan on the subject of church rituals) and the inadequacy of living quarters for the boarding students. A move was begun to locate the school in Port Hope and in September, 1868, it was moved to this city. Two years later the headmaster, Mr. Badgely, and the staff resigned. The same year (1870) the Trinity College Corporation recommended that the head mastership of the Trinity College School be offered to Reverend C. J. S. Bethune. This was done and the school prospered. Bethune stayed with the school for thirty years. Its present location is at Port Hope, Ontario. Father Johnson had two sons at the school while it was at Weston, Arthur Jukes Johnson (Johnson Max) and Jimmy Johnson (Johnson Minor). Jimmy was the namesake of Dr. James Bovell.

17

FIGURE 4. Rev. Charles H. Badgely, Headmaster at Weston. Published in *Trinity College School Record,* F. J. Wainwright, ([Ed.], Port Hope, Ontario, 1915.)

attracted the attention of Ellen and Featherstone Osler. At the time William Osler arrived, January 18, 1866,[2] the headmaster, an Englishman, the Reverend C. H. Badgely, was determined to model the school on the lines of the English public schools such as Eton and Rugby. He decreed that top hats were to be the proper costume, though they must have "looked a bit irregular upon the rough Canadian landscape." The cane, a concrete symbol of discipline, was wielded often and with much "verve."[3] The headmaster was affectionately known among the boys as "Pontius Pilate."

A description of the school as it was in 1867 has been given by a former student.[4]

> The school house was a plain old brick house, facing east, containing a basement and two stories. In the basement was the lower study, where the small boys were supposed to work in the evenings by the light of a coal oil lamp which hung from the ceiling. Adjoining this was a room which, as far as I could learn, was used for tubs on Saturday nights, and sometimes for fights in the daytime, when secrecy had to be observed. The housekeeper's rooms were adjacent, and on the opposite side was the kitchen, which debauched into a woodshed where the winter's supply of wood was kept.
>
> On the ground floor, the dining room occupied the whole of one side, and in this room morning and evening prayers were said. In addition to the Head's room there was on this floor also the upper study, where the big boys were supposed to study, also lighted by a coal oil lamp hanging from the ceiling. In this and the lower study were all the lockers that the boys had. Upstairs were the dormitories. The parsonage nearby was the home of the Reverend Johnson and served as a place of domicile for about half the boys. There arose some keen competition between the boys living in the School House

---

[2]"I can see him now," writes one of Osler's schoolmates, "soon after he arrived at the rectory — with a red pocket-handkerchief round his neck and a sling in his hand taking a survey of any chance birds in the garden." (Cushing, vol. I, p. 28) .

[3]A former student has described the headmaster "[he] was good nature itself, notwithstanding that he sometimes wore a fierce look. He was very dark, and his cleanshaven face showed distinctly the area which he was obliged to traverse every morning. He had piercing black eyes and straight and somewhat lowering black eyebrows, which gave a stern appearance to the upper part of his face. Although 'the Head' could wield a cane with skill and effect, he relied more upon the honor of the boys than their fear of punishment." (*Trinity College School Record*, p. 85.)

[4]M. E. D. Armour, K. C.: *Trinity College School Record*. Port Hope, Williamson and Son, 1913.

and those living in the parsonage which "made it easy to get up matches at cricket and football—and fights."

The third establishment was the school house. Let no one suppose that there ever was any confusion between the Schoolhouse and the schoolhouse. Everyone knew at once which was meant, as soon as spoken, although it is impossible to capitalize initial letters in ordinary speech. The schoolhouse was a rough-cast building facing east. We all trooped across the railway to school, and the Parsonage boys came down the railway tracks for the same purpose.

There was no playing ground except for one small field; in the corner of which stood the rudiments or skeleton of a gymnasium, but which had many of the indicia of a gibbet! On the south face (if a framework can have a face) there hung two hempen ropes waving in the autumn wind! At another angle could be seen a trapeze, which might or might not offset the damaging evidence of the hempen ropes, while at another angle could be seen a pair of parallel bars.

FIGURE 5. Osler (on fence — straw hat) on zoological excursion, circa 1866. (From Osler Collection, Academy of Medicine, Toronto. Original at Ontario Agricultural College, Guelph, Ontario.)

Though he did not teach formal courses in the school, the Reverend Mr. Johnson was a man who could stir the imagination of boys, and he had a particular appeal for young William Osler. Father Johnson was interested in biology, or natural history as it was called in those days. William soon became an ardent disciple of Johnson and before long a first class assistant to the clergyman in his scientific investigations. As fortune would have it, it was at Weston that William met James Bovell, who was a close friend of Johnson and a frequent visitor to Weston. A physician by profession and biologist by hobby, Dr. Bovell too had a lasting influence on the young student. Osler remained at Weston until the summer of 1867.

> Trin. Col. Grammar School,
> Weston,[5] Jan. 24[,] 1866

Dear Ned

It is a cursed shame that I have not written to you before. Your last letter came a little too late for the govenor [sic] had been to Toronto and made arrangements for me to go to Weston before I got your letter or I think I could have gone to Georgetown[.] I like Weston very well[.] [T]here are twenty two boarders, firstrate chaps[.] [I]t is very different from Mr. Checkley's, it is more like the English schools. We have to get up at half past six[,] lessons for an hour before breakfast then prayers, which are a small service by themselves[,] then school from nine till twelve[,] then dinner (firstrate grub) then we have from 1 till 3 o'clock to play or study[,] then from 3 till five school and then from half past six till seven we say Greek and from seven till ten we study [with] Mr. Badgely in the room all the time, he is a firstrate man himself[.][6] He first went through Trinity College (out here) then he was at Cambridge for two and at Oxford for three years. I have not heard from Charlie[7] since I have been here, he must be lonesome up there now without any of his three friends. Jemmy[8] came out to Weston with me[,] he knows the Johnsons who take care of the boarding department[,] he [Johnson] is the rector of the place, his wife is such a nice woman she will do any[thing] in the world for us, and her two daughters (both married,

---

[5]Weston was nine miles west of Toronto.

[6]Reverend Charles H. Badgely, headmaster at Weston. Graduated Trinity College, M.A., 1864.

[7]Charlie Locke.

[8]Jemmy Morgan.

pity) Mrs. C. and Mrs. E. Miles are splendid women[.]⁹ We are taught
singing every Saturday by a teacher from Toronto.¹⁰ We have rare
old fights with the common school boys and have thrashed them every
time yet and now good by old fellow write soon[.]

I remain

ever your friend

W. Osler

P.S. Address W. Osler Trinity College Gram
School, not Gram. School for there is a
regular grammar school here

This letter, sent to Ned while he was in school in Georgetown,
was written soon after Osler entered Weston. In it he described
the makeup of the school, its rector, and the regular schedule at
the school. Apparently Ned had written suggesting that Osler
go to Georgetown to school, but this suggestion came too late, for
he had already been registered at Weston. Only Jemmy Morgan,
of his "Barrie" friends, was with him there. Charlie Locke had
gone elsewhere to school. Much as the school boys of today, Osler
was a little careless with his spelling: "It was clear that even in his
youth words so ran from his pen that it was left for others to dot
the *i*'s and cross the *t*'s for him."

Feb. 28/66

Dear Ned¹¹

I had been expecting a letter from you and was very glad to get
one. We have had great fun at some theatricals we had for the school
liberary [sic][.] [T]hey went off splindidly [sic][and] we had such jolly fun. There were about 200 people from Toronto [and] all Trin-
ity¹² turned out. This is a regular English school[,] all the old English
rules and Mr. Badgely is such a splendid fellow[.]¹³ I wish to the
devil you were here Ned[,] these are such a fine set of fellows and we
have such splendid rows with the vilagers [sic], last Thursday afternoon we got a half holiday and sallied down for a spree[.] [W]e first

---

⁹Mrs. Charles and Edward Miles, daughters of the Reverend Mr. Johnson.

¹⁰Mr. Sefton was the singing teacher from Toronto — "a jolly Englishman."

¹¹Ned was still at Georgetown.

¹²Trinity College, Toronto.

¹³The boys wore top hats much as they did in English schools. Cushing points out
that these top hats must have put the boys at Weston at a disadvantage during a
snow battle with the town boys.

thrashed the common school[14] and then began to pelt the sleighs. [A] lot of us got on one sleigh and as we were passing a fence there was a rooster setting on a fence[.] I had a jolly snowball in my hand and I let drive and knocked him over[.] [T]here was a devil of a rumpus but they did not find out who did it and on last Friday I was coming up and the Roman Catholic school was standing about 80 yards from the road and I bet a boy I could throw and break a window[.] [T]he other fellow threw and did not come near it[.] But I was not so lucky for mine went through the window and struck one of the boys on the head, there was a terrible row about it but I went down to the old Priest and made it all right and put in the window[.] I heard from home the other day and they told me that Frank had got a situation in a factory at Melvile [sic] in Masachusests [sic] [.] [H]e has been all through the states lately down in New York and all about there[.]

     I must stop now Ned for it is ten o'clock and I must be off to bed[.]

I remain your true friend<br>W Osler

Osler's athletic prowess was well known, especially his ability to throw a ball or rock with deadly aim. Cushing quotes one of Osler's schoolmates saying "he established a record in throwing the cricket ball."[15] Milburn stated that he once threw a cricket ball one hundred and fifteen yards, which was a world record at that time.[16] Indeed, Osler was excellent in most sports. In later life he delighted in regaling his young friends with tales of his ability to deliver a thrown missile any place he desired. Cushing quotes one of Osler's friends who had written concerning an incident in which she had dared Sir William to throw a stone and hit something that was a long way off. He hit the object "dead center" with the first stone. Osler then told of the time that he was on his way to school and Ned Milburn dared him to hit a pig with a stone. The pig was a distance away, but he hit it behind the ear, killing the animal instantly. His father had to pay the farmer who owned the pig eight dollars. Osler would break into peals of laughter when he described how the unfortunate pig first looked stunned and then rolled over dead.

---

[14]Apparently there, as in Dundas, a continuous war raged between the pupils attending the common school and those in the grammar school (boarders) .

[15]Cushing, vol. I, p. 35.

[16]Milburn to Cushing, Cushing Archives.

It was at Weston that one of the more notorious incidents in
the life of Willie Osler took place.[17] On April 8, 1866, the Toronto
*Globe* carried the headlines: WESTON SCHOOL PUPILS TURNED OUT-
LAWS AND FUMIGATE THE MATRON WITH SULPHUR. Everyone has
agreed that William conceived and effected the plan to get even
with an unpopular matron of the school. After a specific injustice (the disliked female the day before having upset a pail
of "slops" on the stairs which doused one of the boys), William
and his followers barricaded the woman in her room. They then
concocted a mixture of pepper, mustard, and molasses which was
placed on a stove in the room below. The fumes were carefully
directed through a pipe with the outlet opening into the victim's
room above. The frightened woman stuffed the holes with clothes,
but the boys, using long sticks, soon cleared the vent. She even
attempted to sit on the outlet, but here again, the sticks rendered
her position untenable and her cries of anguish could be heard.
She was finally rescued by the headmaster. Undoubtedly the boys
were treated to a good dose of the hickory stick, but this proved
insufficient to appease the irate lady. She demanded nothing less
than their arrest for assault and battery; so it came to pass that
William and his accomplices spent some time in the Toronto jail.
William's elder brother, Featherstone, ably defended the young
culprits. They received a reprimand together with a fine of $1.00
and court costs, which ended the incident. But the victory was for
the boys, as the matron did not return to the school. William's
mother, Ellen, usually indulgent in such matters, took notice of
the affair in a letter to her son and reprimanded him for bringing
the Osler name into public notice in such a disreputable manner.

Another and milder version of this incident has been given by
Father Johnson's oldest son, Arthur Jukes Johnson (who was a
participant):

> The removal of the school from the parsonage to the building east
> of the G[rand T[runk] R[ailway] track on Church Street necessi-
> tated the employment of someone who could live in this building
> and look after the school's interests.
> The position was at once filled by an old lady and her daughter, both
> large women—the mother an old woman, the daughter of an uncertain

[17]Cushing, vol. I, p. 24.

age. School was held in the room immediately below the large front
room on the second floor in which these ladies sat in the afternoon,
and a pipe-hole passed through the ceiling of the school and the floor
of their room. On almost the first occasion in which four or five boys
were kept in on a half-holiday, they discovered this pipe-hole was at
times not covered. Naturally, such an opportunity to make this a mark
through which paper darts, etc. could be shot was at once seized upon, more particularly as the afore-said maiden lady, notwithstanding
her qualities, was not appreciated by the boys. Things, no doubt, were
said, the ladies probably had the first say, and, of course, had the last.
The engagement lasted probably half-an-hour, as the boys understood
it, an amusing episode which served to pass away an otherwise tedious
hour of detention. Imagine our surprise when the school was served
with a summons which stated that certain boys were charged with having committed an aggravated assault on a certain maiden lady, by
which grievous bodily harm had been sustained.
The plaintiff in this action had rather too fertile an imaginaton, and
this fact led to an acquital. As she endeavoured to convince the magistrate that having been much annoyed by various articles that these
small boys shot up through the pipe-hole, she had used a large square
board to cover the opening; that upon this she had seated herself, and
that while in this position a log of wood of immense size was thrown
with such accuracy that it in some way passed through the pipe-hole,
carrying the board and herself up into the air and causing the dam-
ages complained of. The magistrate looked upon it as a joke.[18]

In spite of his effervescent spirit and propensity for practical
jokes, William continuously excelled in scholarship as well as
athletics and was eventually made Head Prefect at Weston. Cushing states that Osler, despite his ebullience, was described by his
contemporaries as "being so straightforward, manly, and clean
that he exerted an excellent influence on the morale of the
school." Indeed, at the end of the spring term of 1866 he was
head of his class and had received the Chancellor's Prize. Father
Johnson persuaded him to stay another year at the school, along
with Jones "Max,"[19] although both were then eligible to enter
college.

---

[18]*Trinity College School Record.* Port Hope, Williamson and Son, 1913.

[19]The Christian names of the boys at the school were ignored and nicknames were
discouraged. Therefore, when there were two boys with the same name, *viz.* Jones,
they were quickly dubbed Jones Maximus or Jones Minor, whichever was older.

FIGURE 6. Ned Milburn at Trinity College, circa 1868. (Courtesy of Miss Grace Evans of Toronto.)

Weston[,] March 22nd [1866]

Dear Ned

I got your letter just this minute and it just got me in a writing humor[.] I have just written to Jemmy[20] and to my Brother Frank[.] He seems to be getting on very well but has not yet stopped sowing his wild oats. I cannot go till the 12 of April because the holidays are not till then being set by Trinity College and not by the school but if you would write and tell me the precise morning you are coming down I will meet you at the Weston station[.] O Ned I wish you would come to Weston[,] Badgley is the best fellow I ever met without exception and I get on much better than under old Check and if you would tell me when you are coming back from your Holidays I might see you in Toronto. I am not going home but to my uncles[21] at L[l]oydtown and will be in Toronto on the 12 of April and will stay at Jemmy's and I wish you would meet me there if you possibly coul[d] and I would introduce you to some boys who will be your college chums and we will have a gay time at Jemmy[s] room[.] I must stop as I have my Greek Test to get up[.]

Believe me your ever affec[.] Friend[,]

W. Osler

Ned entered Trinity College in the fall of 1866 as Osler fully expected to do, but subsequent events delayed his going until one year later.

Weston[,] May 9th [1866]

Dear Ned

I got your letter on Saturday night[.] I am sorry you are not well but I hope you will be better soon. I am afraid you are a naughty [boy] carrying [on] a correspondence with young ladies[.] Jemmy was out here nearly all last week and we had gay times. You seem to be dead on Concerts up there. I am putting in pretty hard [studies] this quarter[.] We have got a friend of yours I think for Second Master[,] Mr. Evans from Richmond Hill.[22] I suppose you know Miss Gilbert your sister[']s governess[.] She was at Lloydtown at Uncles for a long time she is a very nice girl[.] I was at Lloydtown in the holiday and had a good time. Hang it Ned I don't know how you manage to write such long (Curse it I am cracked) letters (not that I don't like them) but I can[']t write at all[.] We will have gay times at Trinity.

[20]Probably Jemmy Morgan.

[21]Reverend H. B. Osler, youngest brother of Featherstone Osler, lived at Lloydtown, 36 miles north of Toronto.

[22]Richmond Hill — sixteen miles north of Toronto.

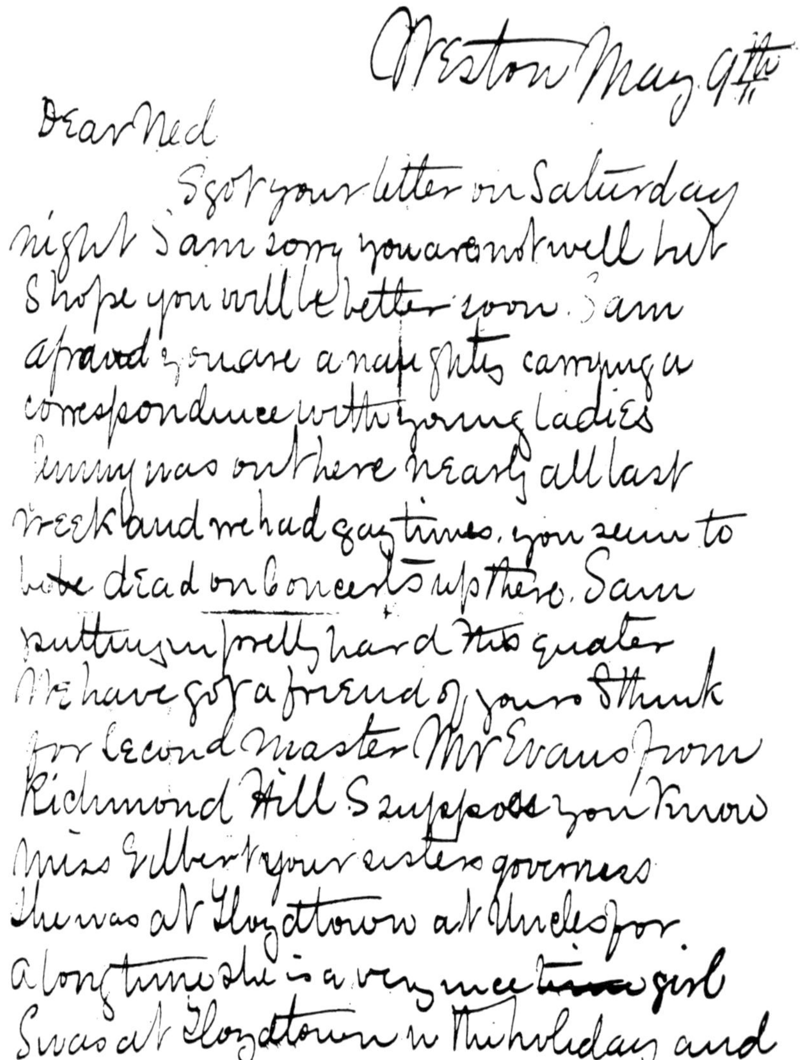

FIGURE 7. Letter to Ned Milburn written during the school year 1866 while Osler was in school at Trinity College Grammar School. From the Reynolds Historical Library in the University of Alabama in Birmingham, Medical Center.

had a good time Hang it Ned I dont
Know how you manage to write such
long ~~times~~ (cause of Sam cracked) letters
(nor that I dont like them) but I cant
write at all We will have gay times
at Trinity. Sam is well sure that
Jimmy is coming up with us for
~~Trinity~~ I must stop Ned for it is bed
time

    Believe me your friend till death

         Willie O

P.S. I have just been looking over
your letter and see that you asked
me to write a long letter and not the
the dinner bell stop me but I had written
five letters then and it was just dinner
time so I had to stop

I am pretty sure that Jemmy is coming up with us for Divinity[.] I
must stop Ned for it is bed time[.]

Believe me your friend till death[,]<br>
Willie

P[.]S. I have just been looking over your letter and see that you asked
me to write a long letter and not let the dinner bell stop me
but I had written five letters then and it was just dinner time so
I had to stop[.]

Weston[,] May 29th[,] 1866

Dear Ned[23]

I received your letter all right and was going to answer it immediately but I thought you might like to know something about our
games they come of[f] in the Spring and Fall, in the spring on Trinity
Monday and in the fall on St[.] Simon and St[.] Judes day, the spring
ones came off yesterday and notwithstanding the rain on Sunday and
the ground being very wet in the morning the games came off in the
afternoon and were a complete success, there was a great crowd out
from Toronto principally ladies. [Y]ou will see by the programe
[sic] inclosed how many prizes I took. You will be surprised perhaps at
my not taking the hop step & jump but at first hop I sprained
my leg so badly that I would not risk jumping any more so that I did
not go in for the long jump. I tried at the high jump but could not
come it because of my leg. I took the hurdle race of 200 yds all the
hurdles 3 Ft and the last about 4 ft high and 3 Ft across, then I took
the throwing the cricket ball[.][24] I threw it 90 yds but about 3 weeks
ago I threw it 103 yds by Mr[.] Johnson measurement. I took all the flat
races, but I nearly forgot to tell you about the prize for throwing the
cricket ball[.] [I]t was a splendid cricket bat, a [$]4.00 one given by
Mr[.] Parsons of Toronto but the steeple chase was the best fun it was
for a mile & 1/2 over the roughest country we could pick out and across
a branch of the Humber[25] [I]t was awful work, you may remember
perhaps a very long bridge just past Weston the race could nearly
all be seen from it and it was crowded with ladies. The race was
entirely between Johnson[26] and I[.] [W]e kept about even till within

---

[23]Osler was just a month from being seventeen years old when this letter was
written.

[24]Cushing quotes a letter from Osler's mother dated May 30, 1866, in which she
mentions the possibility of his remaining at Weston for another term. She also
comments proudly on his being "first" in so many athletic events, a fact that he
mentions in his letter to Ned.

[25]The Humber river flows by Weston.

[26]Johnson, Max (imus)  (Arthur Jukes Johnson) , elder son of Father Johnson.

FIGURE 8. William Osler while a prefect at Trinity College Grammar School, 1867. (From Cushing papers in Osler Library at McGill University.)

about 100 yds of the Parsonage and then we let out I beat him by about 5 yds but I was awfully used up I nearly fainted I ran in the house and laid down on a sofa and all the young girls from town came round (they thought I had fainted) and were saying "Poor Osler" and one of them stooped down and wiped the perspiration of[f] my face with her handkerchief[.] I tell you what Ned it was gay. And I am awfully tired. I almost forgot to tell you Ned that I may not go up to Trinity next year all the Professors of Trinity advise Jones and I to stay another year[.][27] [T]hey say we are too young[.] I am sorry but I think it will be much better[.][28]

I have not time to write more and you must excuse the writing for it is not of the best[.]

Believe me your friend<br>
till Death<br>
Willie

He did exceptionally well in the sporting events mentioned in this letter. The Toronto *Leader* reported that he was winner in the majority of the athletic contests, i.e. the hurdle race, the 200 and 400 yard flat races, the 100 yard hop race, the mile steeple chase, and throwing the cricket ball.[29]

TRINITY COLLEGE GRAMMAR SCHOOL,<br>
Weston, June 24th [1866]

Dear Ned[30]

I suppose you will think that I have forgotten you entirely, but I will not do that in a hurry. I have been so infernally busy preparing for our Midsummer Examination that I have not had time to write[.] I have been studying all this week from ½ three in the morning till 11 o'clock at night, and this afternoon being Saturday I had a game cricket and a swim but blast it all[.] I have 2 hours drill after tea which will completely use me up[.] Jemmy Morgan has been a re-cruiting officer during these late rows with the Fenians[31] and Char-

---

[27]Prefects for 1865-66 at Weston were R. J. Wilson, William Osler, L. K. Jones, F. J. Hellwell. Osler, Head Prefect, at Weston 1866-67, Wilkinson, Anne: *Lions in the Way*. Toronto, Macmillan, 1956, p. 125, and Cushing, vol. I, p. 32.

[28]Osler remained at Weston for an additional year.

[29]Cushing, vol. I, p. 35.

[30]Ned is still at Georgetown in school and was to enter Trinity College in the fall of 1866. Osler originally thought he would go with Ned to Trinity but he was persuaded to wait another year because of his age.

[31]The Fenian Society, a pro-Irish and a fanatically anti-British group, was founded in the United States in 1858. They advocated the invasion and subjection of

ley[32] has been "wandering to and fro seeking Fenians to devour" and I have not been able to keep track of him[.] I do not know where he is now. Mr. Evans[33] our Second Master has been off to the front and Prof Jones[34] of Trinity [College] has been out here for about a week[.] We are going to have an awful Examination at Midsummer[.] I am studying for four prizes but I don't know how I am going to stand. I hope you will come on ahead of all those who go up at October[.] I am sorry that I am not going up but Mr. Badgeley and Dr Bovel[l] say I am too young[.] I think there [sic] will be a very good year[.] A[.] Johnson[35] is going up and he a first rate fellow[.] I suppose you will be going down to Oakville soon[.] Our breaking up day is the 24th of July just one month from today. Do you remember the 20th and 21st last year Especially the evening of the 20th[.] Poor little Philip on a dead drunk[.] I will never forget that night and then the next morning taking the beer barrel home[.] The ship that Frank sailed in from Boston caught fire at sea but luckily it was near some town in Rhode Island and they put it out in there.[36] They have got repaired and started since[.]

I must stop now Ned for I have got 3 more letters to write. When you write tell me when you are coming down and I will be at the station to see you[.]

Believe me your affec. friend<br>W. Osler

Dundas[,] Sept. 4th [1866]

Dear Ned[37]

I have just got your letter[.] I would have got it before but some young ladies who are staying here got it and kept it from me for about 3 hours.[38] Now Ned you must excuse me for not writing for

---

Canada which was to be used as a base of operations against England. Late in 1865 the Society split into two factions — one advocating action in Ireland while the other faction still favored invasion of Canada. In May 1866, six hundred Fenians led by John O'Neill crossed the Niagara River and on June 2, 1866, engaged the Canadian forces sent to intercept them. This engagement was later known as the Battle of Ridgeway.

[32]Charlie Locke, "the wild Irishman."

[33]Reverend Lewis Evans. "Has been off to the front" may refer to the skirmish with the Fenians, or simply that he had been visiting on the lakeshore, generally called "the front" by those living inland in Ontario.

[34]Professor William Jones — nickname "Polly" — a kindly bachelor and mathematics teacher at Trinity College, 1863-95.

[35]Arthur Jukes Johnson (Johnson Max).

[36]Frank Osler had quit school and gone to sea.

[37]Osler and Ned were at home for the summer vacation.

[38]Osler's cousins from England, Jeanette and Marian Osler, were visiting the Featherstone Oslers at the Dundas rectory in 1866.

what between Croquet, shooting and being away from home I have
not had much time[.] I have been playing Croquet nearly every day
since I came home and have been out shooting a great deal[.] I was
out this afternoon and shot 2 ducks[,] 1 rice hen and 5 black squir-
rels and I have been away at Brantford for a couple of days[.] I went
up with Mr. Ballard (the governers [sic] curate) to a picnic and the
opening of an Indian Church[.] I met some very nice girls and had
great fun. I was away nearly all last week shooting[.] I did not get
much for it was raining nearly all the time. Now Ned about your going to Weston[.] I will tell you what I think of it[.] [Y]ou might
like it and you might not[.] I think you would like Mr Badgely and
Mr Johnson[,] but you would have to obey Prefects younger and
smaller than yourself[,] which I think will run against your grain
and the school is conducted on an entirely different principles from
those which you have attended[.][39] I would like myself very much to
have you there for some things and for some I would not[.] I would
not like to have to report you or give you an imposition (For I am
the Head Prefect) and would have to do so if you were a naughty
little boy[.] But Ned I think you are sure of a Scholarship there are
not many going up there will not be more than 8 or ten you need not
be afraid of the two going from Weston[,] Johnson Max and Wilson[.][40] Johnson will have hard work to pass and Wilson has not
much chance for a scholarship[.] I think myself you are almost certain of the £50 one for I do not know anyone as well prepared[.]
I do not think either MacKenzie or Whitaker[41] are going up. Why
actually Prof Ambrey[42] wanted me to go up this year and told the gov-
ener [sic] that I was shure [sic] of one of the high Scholarships (judg-
ing from my papers at Weston) We heard from Frank a few days
ago[.] [H]e has been down to South America on a whaleing [sic] voy-
age and is going off again soon I think[.] I must stop now for this is an
unusually long letter for me to write[.] I enclose a photo[.]

Believe me your affec. friend<br>
W. Osler

I will write again and tell you the day I am going down[.]

---

[39]The school at Weston was conducted on a "prefect" system in which the boys
participated in a student government.

[40]Probably Robert Wilson, classmate of Osler at Weston. He was one of the boys
charged in the Weston assault case along with Osler.

[41]E. Whitaker — classmate at Weston. Probably son of Reverend George Whitaker,
Provost of Trinity College, Toronto. There is no George McKenzie listed among
Trinity College Grammar School students for this session. A Private George Mc-
Kenzie was listed as wounded in left arm in the Battle of Ridgeway. *Troublous
Times in Canada*. Macdonald, J. A. Toronto, 1910. p. 53.

[42]Professor John Ambrey — Professor of Classics at Trinity College, 1863-75. He
was instrumental in establishment of Trinity College Grammar School at Weston.

TRINITY COLLEGE SCHOOL.
Weston, Oct 9[,] 1866

Dear Ned

I got your letter today and as I have a little spare time this evening I am going to answer it[.] Johnson told me you were up for your Examination[.][43] I hope you have done well[.] I am almost sorry now that I did not go up this year it is such a good one you will have a jolly time[.] I heard from Jemmy last Saturday he has had to cane one boy[.][44] I though[t] that he would have to begin thrashing soon[.] We play a great deal of cricket here now and have quite a good eleven[.] [S]ome of the new boys play very well[.] I should not be surprised if we should challenge the second eleven of Trinity next summer. That was quite true what Johnson told you about a man going to shoot one of us[.] [H]e was half drunk at the time. Our Fall Games come off on the 18th of this month[.] I will be pressed pretty hard in my running this time for some of the new boys run very well[,] but I will do my best[.] [Y]ou will have a good chance at the Trinity races on St Simon and St Judes [day][45] Mr Badgley is going to give a large pewter for the Steeple Chase and I hope you will get it. I will give that young lady's message to my cousin[46] when I see him next[.] Remember me to McKenzie when you see him[.][47]

Believe me your affec
friend
W. Osler

TRINITY COLLEGE SCHOOL,
Weston, Oct 26[,] 1866

Dear Ned[48]

I got your letter all right and was very glad of it for I wanted to hear how you like College life[.] [Y]ou must have a gay time according to Johnson who was out last Sunday[,] What a jolly lark that routing must be[.] I suppose you will give it to us when we are first year men[.] I am sorry you did not take a Scholarship but you will have better luck next time I hope[.] [D]id you see an account of our cricket match in the Wednesday Leader(?) [W]e gave the Toronto fellows a good thrashing didn't we. You must run next Monday Ned I'm sure you will do well the only one you need be afraid is Cum-

---

[43]Arthur Jukes Johnson entered Trinity College along with Milburn in 1866.

[44]Jemmy Morgan was now headmaster of Oakville Grammar School, Oakville, Ontario. Oakville was half the distance between Dundas and Toronto.

[45]Ned Milburn won the competitive races and set a distance record for the next three years.

[46]Probably a cousin, W. P. Osler, who was at Weston School with W. Osler.

[47]Evidently McKenzie went up to Trinity College after all. See letter of June 24, 1866.

[48]Ned was now at Trinity College.

berland and I think you can beat him at any rate you can try. Our
games come off on the Thursday after[.] I do not know how I will do
for there are a great many to compete with[.] We are going to have
a large shine the same evening at which we expect to have some fun.
We are all coming in to Convocation whenever it is[.][49] I heard from
Jemmy lately he is quite settled at the Fletchers and seems to be doing very well he sent me a barrel of apples this week and sad to say
they are all gone[.][50] A Barrel is not much among nearly 50 boys[.]
Hang it I'm sorry I did not go up this year but its no good crying over
spilt milk[.] I must stop now for it is bed time[.]

    Remember me to Johnson Max

Believe me your affec friend<br>W. Osler

    The following letter was written by Ned to Osler after learn-
ing that he was ill. Arthur Jukes Johnson apparently was the
source of the information. Osler had received a severe injury to
his leg during Rugby scrimmaging in the Autumn of 1866.[51] He
developed osteomyelitis and was incapacitated for a long period.

Trin. Coll.<br>Nov. 27[,] 66

Dear Willie,[52]

    I am very sorry to hear that you are so ill, I never heard any-
thing about it till just now, when Johnson in the coolest manner
possible tells me that you are seriously ill, I don't know whether to
believe him or not but I think I must for this very likely will account
for your not writing to me. I do hope and trust however that it will
not be very serious. I hear that you are going to Oakville as soon as
your School breaks up. Won't we have a glorious time?[53] I did wish,
and fully intended to ask you to come and stay with me a short time
at Xmas but Jimmie has anticipated me; any way it will be all right

---

[49]Apparently the entire student body and faculty at Trinity College Grammar
School attended the Convocation at Trinity College in Toronto.

[50]Reverend John Fletcher, rector of an Oakville Church, tutored Osler for his
college entrance exams in the summer of 1867 so that he might try for a scholarship. Jemmy Morgan and Osler were in the same house for the summer of 1866.
Another prefect from Weston was there also, L. K. Jones. After studies were over
at night, they would examine specimens for long hours under a microscope
borrowed from Dr. Bovell.

[51]Cushing, vol. I, p. 41.

[52]From the Cushing Archives — Osler Library, McGill University.

[53]Osler spent the summer of 1867 in Oakville. See letter of Osler to Milburn dated
October 26, 1866.

for I don't intend him to monopolise you altogether although he says he will, we'll see about that.

I can promise you plenty of good shooting, for there are lots of Quail, partridges and rabbits to be found; but this is not half, there are a great many other things to be considered. I don't think we will have an examination this Xmas and so I will be able to get away sooner[.] I only hope you won't be gone before I get home. I am getting on very well, altho' I am not working as hard as I ought to. I find it very hard on account of the rows that take place nearly every night, as soon as the fellows get thro' their lectures they adjourn to some of the second year men's rooms and after drinking, Singing and smoking, proceed to the doors of the Chapel and there have a regular hoedown, I hardly approve of the place they have chosen, for I do not think it quite right. They will be pretty well quieted down by the end of next term because the June exam, will then soon be coming on and they will have to work hard. I hope you will take a Scholarship when you come up, I am sure you will if you work hard and steadily. Jemmie is very sick I don't know what it is, but I suppose *fever and ague* as usual. I won't ask you to write to me, not that I wouldn't be overjoyed to hear from you, but because it might give you a great deal of trouble and keep you from getting better sooner. Don't *dare* to leave Oakville without my Seeing you.

Believe me dear Willie

ever your most affect.
friend Ned

TRINITY COLLEGE SCHOOL
Weston, Jan. 20th[,] 1866 [probably 1867]

Dear Ned

I am really ashamed of myself for not writing to you before but you must forgive me for I have been so busy all through the Christmas Holidays and when there are four girls in the house one does not feel inclined for doing much writing.[54] I had intended to come to Oakville a week from last Friday and stay overnight with Jemmy but my leg was not so well, so I had to put of[f] going till Saturday when Jemmy met me in the train. How have you enjoyed your Christmas Holidays[?] I hope you did not flirt too much with the girls. My leg did not allow me to go out at all till about a week before the Holidays ended so that I had no skating[.] It is not quite well yet though it is getting better rapidly. You did not go back to Trinity till Monday[.] [O]ne of our fellows told me he came up in the train with you. I hope you are going to do well in your June Examinations and I hope you will study hard[.] I will be in town on Tuesday or Wed-

---

[54]Osler's cousins were still visiting at the rectory.

nesday but will not have time to go up to the College to see you for
I have a great many things to do in town. When you write tell me all
about Trinity time, what you do in the morning and what you do
in the afternoon. I hear Anderson and Jones were plucked[.] [W]hat
sort of a fellow is Jones, not Polly Jones but C. Jones[?] [B]y the by
how is that little whippersnapper[,] he has not shown his ugly face
out here this term yet. That was a nasty thing the Provost losing his
daughter[.]⁵⁵ I suppose you all went to the funeral. There is not much
doing out here now but work[.] The snow is too dry for snowballing
or we might have some rows[.] I heard from Jemmy the day before
yesterday he seems quite blooming[.] Tell Johnson⁵⁶ I was going to
write to him this afternoon, but am too seedy and tell him "that Mr.
C. Miles wants his meerschaum at once"⁵⁷ and tell him I will write
some time towards the end of the week[.] Write soon[.]

Believe me ever your friend<br>W. Osler

Trin. Coll. School

In March 1867 the British Parliament passed the "North
American Act" thereby uniting all Canada under a central government, and on July 1, 1867, the Dominion of Canada was officially
created. It has been stated that Canada became a nation because
her people did not wish to be swallowed up by her burgeoning
southern neighbor, the United States.

The injury to Osler's leg gave him an unusual opportunity to
work more closely with Father Johnson on his biological collection. The minister rigged up a chair rest for the injured leg, and
during Osler's period of inactivity he had more opportunity to
study the specimens under the microscope. Here also he came to
have a closer relationship with Dr. Bovell, who, as the school's
physician, treated Osler's injury.

THE PARSONAGE,<br>St. Philip's, Weston, C.W.

April 4th [1867]

Dear Ned

I am almost ashamed to begin to write to you now, for I feel that
I have neglected you altogether but you must forgive me Ned this

---

⁵⁵George Whitaker, Provost of Trinity College (apparently his daughter died).

⁵⁶Arthur Jukes Johnson (Johnson Max).

⁵⁷Mr. C. Miles, son-in-law of Reverend Johnson.

time and for the time to come I promise better behaviour. I heard from Jemmy yesterday and he wants me to stay at Oakville for two or three days on my way home but I am afraid I cannot for we have only a little over a weeks holiday's[.][58] I go home next Thursday and come back a week from next Saturday[,] but I think I will stay over the Thursday night. I was so sorry that I was not able to come in to Town while the "Wild Irishman" was there[.][59] I should have so liked to have seen him but I could not possibly get in. I hope you are grinding hard for your June Exam[.] You must try and get a Scholarship[,] if you work hard I know you will get one. Our Easter Ex comes on Next Tuesday. I think Polly[60] and Ambrey are going to examine us[.] I hope the villians don't give us a hard one like they did last Easter. We had a jolly supper at Badgleys on Sunday evening[.] I have just written to Johnson[61] and he will give you this if he does not forget. When do you go home? Before or after us. [I]f you go on Thursday we will go up together[.]

> Write before next Thursday
> Believe me ever your affec. friend
> W. Osler

So Osler left Weston, but the seeds of his future interest in science had been well planted. He did not forget Father Johnson and Weston. Johnson visited him at his home in Dundas during the summer of 1867 and the two continued their nature studies. Osler never forgot Father Johnson and Weston, and maintained a warm correspondence with Johnson until the latter's death in 1880.

---

[58] Jemmy Morgan.
[59] Charlie Locke.
[60] "Polly" Jones taught mathematics at Weston.
[61] Arthur Jukes Johnson (Johnson Max).

# V

# Trinity College

*My first impulse was to thank God that he had heard my prayer and inclined one of my six boys to make choice of that as his path in life.\**

O sler entered Trinity College in the fall of 1867. Enrollment at the opening of this term was the smallest in the history of the college, with only four matriculants; three of these young men were from Trinity College Grammar School at Weston. Milburn had been at Trinity for one year, having entered in the fall of 1866. The atmosphere of the college at the beginning of the fall session of '67 was somber and sad as the revered founder of the college, Bishop Strachan, was fatally ill. He died a few days later.

The school was uninviting to such an active young enthusiast as Osler. The buildings were uncomfortably cold, and their appearance was bleak and austere. There were strict regulations that were considered necessary for young men preparing for work in the church. Bars had been placed on the windows of the basement and ground floor in order to curb the numerous escapades of unlawful flight to dances, the theatre and other nocturnal social pleasures. These restrictions must have been particularly galling to the fun-loving Osler.

Osler's extra year at Weston had served him well. He had won the Dixon Prize Scholarship at Trinity College. Osler appeared destined to enter the Anglican priesthood, for that was the prime objective of training at Trinity College. However, his overpowering interest had now become science which had been nurtured by Father Johnson and Dr. Bovell. Innocently and unconsciously,

---

*Ellen Osler to William, Dundas, Ontario, May 30, 1866. As quoted in *Lions in the Way*, Toronto, Macmillian, 1956, p. 125.

they had led their young friend into the study of biology and away
from that of the ministry.

58

Clarke, Christopher.
5 Greene, Richard.
Hamilton, George W.
Jones, Charles Jerome.
Jones, Henry Osborne.
Walker, Thaddeus.
8 Mackenzie, George Allan.
4 Ball, Clarence Widmer.
6 Doherty, Robert.
2 Paterson, Thomas Wilson.
Coleman, Abel Henry.
Hagarty, Arthur Edmund.
Hamilton, George.
Johnson, Arthur Jukes.
Low, Rev. George Jacob.
7 MacNab, Allan Napier.
Matheson, Alan Frederick
Milburn, Edward Fairfax.
Whitaker, Ernest.
5 Cox, Isaac Gregory.
9 Harman, Lloyd, C. A.M.
3 Jarvis, Arthur.
2 Osler, William.
Jones, Louis Kossuth.
10 Armstrong, Thomas.

(2) Dickson Scholar. (3) Bishop Strachan Scholar. (4) Burnside Scholar.
(5) Cameron Scholar. (6) Allan Scholar. (7) Cooper Exhibitioner.
(8) Wellington Scholar. (9) Foundation Scholar. (10) Church Society
Exhibitioner.

FIGURE 9. From Calendar of University of Trinity College, Toronto, for
1868. (Courtesy of Trinity College, Toronto.)

After Osler's matriculation at Trinity he continued his close
association with Dr. Bovell, visiting him often in his home and
helping him prepare the catalogue for his biological specimens.
He also accepted Dr. Bovell's invitation to attend his lectures at
the Toronto Medical School.

Osler's scientific interests now occupied most of his time and
thoughts. Weekends and vacations found him back in Weston
diligently acquiring, identifying and cataloguing new specimens

for Johnson's and Bovell's zoological collections. He always took an interest in the school activities at Weston, especially in athletics. Osler spent the summer vacation in Dundas, and even there he pursued his scientific interests.

In reflecting on the activities of young Osler during his first year at Trinity, one is not surprised that he summarily announced several days after returning to Trinity for the fall term of 1868 that he was leaving to enter the medical school. Probably this turn of events was not anticipated by his friend Bovell, although when Osler informed him of his intention, he countered, "That's splendid, come along with me." Osler's parents were doubtless disappointed, but not a word of reproach was registered. They had the utmost faith in their children and their prerogative to choose their own vocation.

Very little is known of Osler's stay at Trinity College. His penchant for practical jokes might have been somewhat restrained, but assuredly there was no sudden change in his lively nature. Possibly the heavy work load or the somber atmosphere that pervaded the school after the death of its founder served to discourage any unusual outburst. Certainly he was again closely associated with Ned Milburn. It is hardly conceivable that these two lively spirits could remain subdued for an entire school session.

Cushing assigns the following incident to the time of their stay at Barrie School, but it would seem more likely for it to have occurred while the two boys were together at Trinity, since the locale of the incident is in Toronto. The story is told by Milburn and quoted by Cushing.

One of the last tricks, indeed the last, I think, that we played was on an American who advertised for a wife. In our Toronto newspaper Osler noticed the advertisement and suggested the following plan— to answer the advertisement, describing ourselves as a brunette and a blond respectively—so that he could make [his] choice according to his fancy. We had some trouble in fitting ourselves out with girls' clothes, but with my sister's help we developed into pretty fair specimens of the genus girl. In due time the farmer arrived at the Grand Trunk Station where we had agreed to meet him, for the station we know was badly lighted, which would be of advantage to us. All went well—we resisted his request for another meeting by daylight and asked him to make his choice then and there. He did so, and as he rather liked blondes his choice fell on me. I wonder at it, for Osler made a beautiful girl with his clear-cut features and olive complexion. We never knew what became of the farmer—he left us, promising to return in a month, as this would give him time to fix up his house. I hope he got a blond.

# VI

## Osler Goes to
## The Toronto Medical School

*As soon as I got interested in Medicine I had only
a single idea.*\*

Osler never regretted giving up the ministry for a scientific
career. In later life he was to say, "early in my college life I
kicked over the traces and exchanged the classics for science."[1]

The two years he spent at the Toronto Medical School were
under the special tutelage of Dr. Bovell, with whom Osler made
his home. While there he continued to work on Bovell's protozoan
collection in his spare time and to assist the physician in his office
appointments. He also maintained his close relationship with
The Reverend Johnson at Weston, collecting and preparing specimens for him during weekends and holidays.[2] During the summer
vacation of 1869 he served as an understudy to Dr. A. Holford
Walker, the Oslers' family physician in Dundas, although during
his spare time he continued to hunt specimens for his zoological
collection.

Little is known of Osler's stay at the Toronto Medical School
except his strong attachment to Bovell and Johnson, and the
account of his vigor in studying his newly chosen profession.

---

\**The Albany Medical Annals, xx:*307-9, June, 1899.

[1]*The School World.* London, 1916, pp. 41-44.

[2]Father Johnson visited Osler in Dundas during the summer of 1869 where they
collaborated on zoological specimen hunts. The rectory at Dundas had an excellent
view of the Dundas Marsh through which ran the old Desjardins Canal connecting
Burlington Bay with Dundas. Across the road from the house there was a park
through which ran a footpath leading down to the marsh. This, in all probability,
was the path taken by young Osler and Father Johnson in their peregrinations.

Young Osler entered into the study of medicine with his customary industry and enthusiasm, thereby becoming a highly respected
student at the school. He showed an unusual amount of interest
in anatomy, likely the only laboratory science available at the
school, and spent long hours in the dissecting room. He did much
of his dissecting alone, during odd hours, often working out his
problems without the aid of a demonstrator. It was here that he
identified the *Trichinella spiralis* in the muscles of a cadaver he
was studying.

During the summer vacation of 1870 Osler decided to leave
the Toronto Medical School and enter McGill University Medical
School. The clinical opportunities of the Montreal hospitals were
considered excellent and these facilities were more available to the
medical student than those in Toronto. The move from Toronto
to McGill probably was discussed and approved by Bovell. Bovell
left during the summer for a visit to the West Indies. He left no
hint that he might not return. However, the battle between the
medical and the theological life was decided, and Bovell gave up
the practice of medicine to remain in the West Indies, where he
became a priest in the Anglican Church.

There is little doubt that Osler's association with Bovell had a
profound effect on his future personality. He admired the devo-
tion the medical students showed for the saintly Bovell, but he
also viewed in mature perspective the professor's inability to con-
centrate on a single purpose. The result of this lack was a diffusion
of his efforts which was rarely effective.[3] Cushing states that it was
Dr. Bovell who gave Osler a letter of introduction to Professor
Palmer Howard at McGill, a man who also was to have considerable influence on the young student.

Osler's association with the Reverend Johnson had already influenced his life in more ways than that associated with the study
of science. The rector was constantly embroiled in controversy
with his church superiors and eventually his school at Weston was

[3]Osler later said of Bovell, "He was an omnivorous reader and transmuter; he
could talk upon anything in the science of the day from protoplasm to evolution;
but he lacked concentration and that scientific accuracy which only comes with
long training (sometimes, indeed never comes) and which is the ballast of the
boat."

taken away from him. It has been postulated that Osler was acutely aware of the consequences of the priest's controversies and made certain he always avoided such clashes throughout his life. Certainly one of the outstanding characteristics of Osler's personality was his unique ability to get along with others.

It was at Toronto that the foundation of Osler's lifelong habits was laid. The cornerstone of this foundation was "work," and "the finding of this a pleasure." In an address given later in his life he added to this other qualities of character: the art of detachment, the virtue of method, the quality of thoroughness, and the fourth, to which he attached the greatest importance — the grace of humility![4]

---

[4]"Teacher and Student," an address delivered at the opening of the new medical buildings, University of Minnesota, Minneapolis, October 4, 1892.

# VII

## McGill Medical School

*Our main business is not to see what lies dimly at a distance, but to do what lies clearly at hand.*\*

Osler left Toronto Medical School to enter McGill University Medical School in Montreal in the fall of 1870 for his final clinical years of medical education. The reputation of the school at Toronto had suffered when its faculty was torn by internal dissension. McGill was without doubt the most outstanding medical school in Canada, and probably on the American continent. The school was largely influenced by the Edinburgh traditions and most of the men on the faculty were busy practitioners. Much of the medical curriculum in the school was given by lecture, but the clinical material available to the students at the Montreal General Hospital was of considerable value.

Osler's intimate friends from Barrie, Charlie Locke and Clarkson McConkey, also came to Montreal from the Toronto Medical School for further medical training. They lived together, with other students, on Lower St. Urbain Street and were known locally as the "St. Urbain Clique." This youthful group was also referred to as the "bearded infants."

Osler had been described by one of his fellow students as being small of stature, olive skinned, and very jovial. He could have passed for a "Spaniard"[1] easily. He either had a mustache on arriving or grew one soon after. Osler was not the most brilliant boy in the class, but he soon became known for his industriousness and keen interest. His deep faith and interest in matters of

\*Thomas Carlyle.

[1]Shepard, F. J.: "Osler's Montreal Period," Bulletin No. IX, Inter Ass. of Med. Museums, *Osler Memorial Number*, 1927, Abbott, M. F. (Ed.) . Montreal. Privately Printed. p. 153.

religion continued, as he frequently attended the services at St. John, the Evangelists Anglican Church. This church was directly across the street from the Montreal General Hospital, and Osler became a close friend of the rector, the Reverend Edmund Wood.

Osler's affinity for playing practical jokes on his fellow students had continued, though they were somewhat more subdued than those of the days at Dundas, Barrie, and Weston. Harry Wright, of Ottawa, Osler's roommate, was said to have laughed every time Osler's name was mentioned.[2] Certainly this reflected some memories of practical jokes that Osler had promulgated during their stay in Montreal. He often worked very late in the autopsy room and wards of the hospital, and when he returned to his quarters all of his fellow students were usually asleep. He would proceed to arouse them from sleep with knocks and loud noises. When sufficiently waked and angry they would chase him to his room, only to find the door firmly barred, while inside, laughing, would be the irrepressible Willie Osler!

After his first year at McGill he, along with his roommate Harry Wright, came under the influence of Dr. R. Palmer Howard, a professor at McGill, and they were frequent visitors in his home. Osler spent the summer of 1871 assisting Dr. Howard, who made his extensive library available to the young student. It was in this library that he read a volume of Carlyle and chanced upon the familiar quotation

> Our main business is not to see what lies dimly at a distance but to do what lies clearly at hand.

This statement was to serve as his watchword throughout a long career. Dr. Howard's effect on Osler's career was considerable. Of the three men who taught Osler and were revered by him, John-son, Bovell, and Howard, it was the latter whom he most admired. With Howard, "the study and the teaching of medicine were an absorbing passion."[3]

---

[2]Cushing, vol. I, p. 72.

[3]Osler, in his address "The Student Life," says further of Howard, "An ideal teacher because a student, ever alert to the new problems, and indomitable energy enabled him in the midst of an exacting practice to maintain an ardent enthusiasm still

At McGill, Osler did his first medical writing, for it was customary for the clinical clerk to report the cases of special interest from the Montreal General Hospital in the Canadian Medical and Surgical Journal. Osler reported several cases from Dr. Duncan McCallum's ward.[4] Here also he met Drs. George Ross and F. J. Shepard.[5] who were resident surgeons and who in a few years were to help instill a modern spirit to teaching in the preclinical years.

Osler's English cousins, Mariane[6] and Jennette, had returned to Canada two years previously and lived in Montreal at this time. William first met Jennette Osler, his cousin, in 1866 when she visited her uncle and aunt, Featherstone and Ellen Osler. Jennette was evidently very intelligent, but more, she was pretty and fascinating, and the Osler boys soon fell under her spell. William and Jennette became fast friends, and after his appointment to the McGill faculty she often edited and coached him in the preparation of his lectures. Jennette's love and encouragement did much to benefit Osler's life.

Osler worked long and arduously throughout his stay at McGill, and for graduation he prepared a special exhibit and thesis on pathology. Because of his previous training at Trinity College he was allowed to take his final examinations at the end of his second year. In the list of honors for the Graduating Class of 1872, a special prize was awarded to Osler for his thesis, based largely on original observations and investigations he had made. Unfortunately, the thesis was never published and only a portion has survived.

---

to keep bright the fields which he had lighted in his youth. Since those days I have seen many teachers and have had many colleagues, but I have never known one in whom was more happily combined a stern sense of duty with the mental freshness of youth."

[4]McCallum was Professor of Midwifery at McGill.

[5]F. J. Shepard afterwards became dean at McGill. Shepard said of Osler, "As I observed him in his early days he was always thinking the best of everybody and everything, continuously making new friends, but never forgetting the old ones. To Osler, friendship became a lifelong, absorbing passion." *Memorial Number.* Bulletin No. IX, Inter. Ass. of Med. Museums. Abbott, M. Ed., Montreal, 1927. p. 154.

[6]Mariane married George Francis. Their son, Dr. William Francis, was for a long time curator of Osler Library at McGill. After Osler's death, he also assisted in completing the catalogue of his library.

There are no known letters written to Milburn during this period, although surely he did not forget his friend. Milburn was teaching at Belleville, Ontario. Perhaps Osler found opportunity to visit him on occasion.

W. A. Johnson                              James Bovell

R. Palmer Howard

FIGURE 10. The three men who most influenced Osler's life. (From Cushings's *The Life of Sir William Osler*, Oxford, Clarendon Press, 1925, vol. I, p. 69.)

# VIII

## The Young Professor at McGill
## 1874 - 1884

*Work, and the finding of this a pleasure.**

Osler came to McGill in 1874 as lecturer on the McGill Medical Faculty. He was well prepared for his position, and though the pay was meager, he was enthusiastic and determined to succeed. The diligence with which he entered his work became a dictum in his subsequent career. He was to state later that he possessed but one talent — "a capacity for industry."

His appointment as instructor in the medical school at McGill University carried with it the privilege of private practice, but he was little inclined to this facet of his position. Surely, this would have improved his sadly depleted financial state, but he became so engrossed in his teaching duties that he found little time for anything else. Although his income from the school was meager, he used a portion of it to purchase laboratory supplies for his students, which frequently forced him to seek small loans from his friend Dr. Palmer Howard to meet immediate expenses. He took a position in the smallpox ward of the Montreal General Hospital (one that was not without danger, as he later developed the disease, though fortunately in a mild form) because he wanted the extra income to purchase twelve microscopes for use of the medical students in his laboratory courses.

At the end of the first semester of his first term at McGill, Osler was appointed a professor on the faculty to replace the retiring Dr. Drake. Though he did not hold a staff position in the Montreal General Hospital, he sought out and performed autopsies, and as time passed, more and more of the staff, busy with

*The master word in medicine, *Montreal Med J, 31*:684, 1902.

their private practices, depended on Osler for their postmortem examinations. This was particularly satisfactory to the young professor, for he found the study of pathology of disease very rewarding. His interest and skill in describing morbid anatomical specimens resulted in his being named to the newly created position of pathologist at the hospital in May 1876. Osler had demonstrated the value of such a position and had more than earned the appointment.

His mind, even at this early stage, showed the discipline and order that made it possible for him to grasp so readily each problem that he encountered. Most of his writings reflect his continual eagerness in the pursuit of knowledge, as well as his frequent forth-right opinions. He kept detailed records, thus preserving his observations for further reference. These factors were to be of immense importance to his future accomplishments in the medical world. Fortunately, he also possessed the ability to transmit these attributes to his students, for they too became prolific writers.

In 1880, Osler was saddened at the death of his Barrie chum, Charlie Locke, who had practiced medicine in Hamilton, Ontario. Locke had evidently not made a success financially, as his estate left scant means for the support of his family. Characteristically, Osler unobtrusively assumed the burden of educating Locke's three children.

In the spring of 1878 he actively sought a clinical appointment on the staff of the Montreal General Hospital. It was the custom in both British and Canadian institutions to furnish references for such appointments. Although this procedure was extremely distasteful to him, and he assiduously refrained from doing this in later years, Osler evidently felt that this appointment was essential to his faculty position at McGill; otherwise, he probably would have allowed the opportunity to pass. He was successful in securing the appointment. A petition in his favor from the students at McGill must also have influenced the Board of Governors.

Osler remained an incorrigible practical joker. Cushing relates that on one occasion he visited the home of his friend and colleague, Dr. Adam Wright, unexpectedly. Finding Mrs. Wright telephoning an order to her butcher, he unceremoniously took the telephone and, to the surprise of the unsuspecting butcher and the chagrin of Mrs. Wright, proceeded to berate the unfortunate butcher for supposedly delivering an unusually tough steak the previous day.

It was in Montreal that Osler invented his alter ego, one Egerton Y. Davis, M.D. He frequently used this pen name for practical jokes on his professional colleagues.

While in Montreal Osler remembered his friends of former days. Father Johnson's son Jimmie, Osler's schoolmate from Weston, entered McGill Medical School, where he was befriended by Osler. Father Johnson, however, was never quite reconciled to the secular ways of the University and did not hesitate to criticize them in his letters to Osler. Johnson visited him at McGill on at least two occasions, and it appears that he considered Osler to be the only redeeming feature of McGill. Both Dr. Bovell and Father Johnson died during these years. Jimmy Johnson finished McGill and, probably on the advice of Osler, did postgraduate work in London. We are certain also that he did not forget his friend Ned Milburn. Although the letters for this period were lost, we know that they once existed. Milburn wrote Cushing that he considered the letters from Osler during his early days at McGill most important, inasmuch as they reflected to a great extent the development of the man he was later to become.

Unquestionably, these letters would have told of the famous Dinner Club of which he was a member, the monthly meetings which took place at the homes of the various members in succession, and Osler's pranks, usually achieved at his friends' expense. Some details of Osler's courtship rumored about this time might even have been revealed. It was said that this relationship ended when the father of the lady in question objected to a prospective son-in-law with agnostic leanings and no visible means of support (the lady supposedly never married).

The letters could have told of Osler's appointment as co-editor of the *Canada Medical and Surgical Journal,* and of his election as a Fellow of the Royal College of Physicians, a signal honor for a Canadian and a man of his youth.

Shepard said that the spirit Osler had infused in the school at McGill remained behind him long after he was gone. He never lost interest in his alma mater and "as a touching token of his love for her," he bequeathed her his library and requested that his ashes be deposited with his beloved books.

Osler commented on leaving Montreal that though he was not a rich man in worldly goods, he was "rich in the goods which neither moth or rust are able to corrupt, friendship, good fellowship, wider experience and fuller knowledge."[1]

---

[1]Blackader, A. D.: *Osler Memorial Number,* Bull. No. IX, Inter Ass of Med Museums, Abbott, M. E., (Ed.) , Montreal, 1927, p. 162.

# IX

## Osler Goes to Philadelphia
## 1884 - 1889

*I taught medical students on the wards**

In May, 1884, Dr. Alfred Stille's impending retirement from the Senior Chair of Medicine at the University of Pennsylvania was announced, and it was generally assumed that Dr. William Pepper, another member of the faculty, would succeed him. Immediately, there were a number of proposals for the replacement of Pepper's soon-to-be-vacated Chair of Clinical Medicine. In past years there had been at the Pennsylvania school a tendency in the appointments toward favoring the most capable man in line for the position, and this one was to be no exception, for the Medical Committee of the Board of Trustees had recommended to the Board that a member of the existing teaching staff should be elected to fill this vacancy.

There was at that time published in the city of Philadelphia one of the outstanding medical journals in America, *The Medical News.* Through William Osler's frequent contributions to this publication, he had become known as an eminently qualified investigator and writer. It was at a weekly meeting of the Editorial Staff of this journal that Osler's name was mentioned during a discussion as a possible successor to Dr. Pepper's position. Apparently, none of the men present knew Osler personally, only by reputation and by his many contributions to the medical literature.

The group strongly urged Dr. James Tyson, a prominent

*Osler, Sir Wm.: *Aphorisms from his Bedside* Teachings and Writings. Bean, W. B., (Ed.), Springfield, Thomas, 1961.

member of the Medical College faculty, who was present, to take steps to have Dr. William Osler's name proposed to the Board. Dr. S. W. Gross was also one of those present at this momentous gathering, and later Dr. Osler gave to him much credit for the appointment.

Although Dr. Tyson felt that the hour was late, he finally consented to contact his colleague, Dr. Horatio C. Wood, another member of the school's faculty, concerning the appointment of Osler for this medical school position. This he did, and Dr. Wood was sufficiently interested to set out at once on an unannounced trip to Montreal to learn first hand of Osler's qualifications for the appointment.

Dr. Wood went to Montreal in the summer of 1884 and visited not only Montreal General Hospital, but the French hospitals as well. Through his inquiries he became convinced that Osler was eminently qualified for the position of Clinical Professor of Medicine at the University of Pennsylvania. It is of interest that he returned home without contacting any of Osler's colleagues at McGill. Possibly, this omission was intentional, as he may have felt that the information he had obtained was sufficient without arousing the suspicion of the McGill faculty as to the nature of his visit.

Evidently, the Medical Committee of the Board of Trustees of the University of Pennsylvania was equally impressed with Dr. Wood's report, for Dr. Tyson wrote Osler a letter inquiring whether he would accept the position if it were offered. Osler at this time was visiting clinical centers in Europe and the letter was forwarded to him by his old friend Dr. Shepard of the McGill faculty. Osler, who had played so many practical jokes on his colleagues, was at first suspicious of the letter. He thought possibly Shepard and his friends were at long last having some fun at his expense. However, on becoming convinced that the letter was genuine, and acting on the advice contained in Dr. Tyson's letter, he sent a telegram to Dr. S. Weir Mitchell, a well known faculty member of the Philadelphia school who was visiting London, saying he would accept the appointment. The story of his indecision about leaving McGill is now well known — that while visiting the medical school in Leipzig, Germany, this was finally settled with the flip of a coin.

Dr. Mitchell arranged to see him in London so as to appraise not only his scientific accomplishments, but also his social graces. As Osler later related the story, one of the tests that Dr. Mitchell subjected him to was on how to dispose of the cherry stones while eating cherry pie!

Mitchell was obviously quite favorably impressed, for he immediately began the dispatch of a number of laudatory letters in Osler's behalf to men of influence on the faculty at the University of Pennsylvania.[1]

The McGill faculty, now thoroughly alarmed over the possible loss of Osler, began to stir itself, though belatedly, and some time that summer Dean Palmer Howard wrote Osler that the faculty proposed to establish a Chair of Pathology and Comparative Pathology, which he offered to Osler at an annual stipend of $1,600. This offer came too late, for Osler had already firmly committed himself to the appointment in Philadelphia.

Apparently the Editorial Staff of *The Medical News* was taking no chances of any undue pressure being applied to keep Osler in Montreal, for on August 9, 1884, there appeared the following item in this medical publication:

> Dr. William Osler, of McGill University, Montreal, is prominently and favorably mentioned in connection with the Professorship of Clinical Medicine at the University of Pennsylvania, rendered vacant by the transfer of Dr. Pepper to the Chair of Theory and Practice of Medicine. Dr. Osler is widely known as a talented scholar, a learned clinician and a popular teacher, and his election, which it is understood will be very acceptable to the Medical Faculty, would add undoubtedly to the high reputation which the University has already enjoyed.

Osler had sought to keep the news of his leaving a secret, but by the time he returned from Europe his impending departure from McGill was well known. A few weeks later he was elected president of the Canadian Medical Association at their annual

---

[1]One of these letters, addressed to A. L. S. (probably Dr. Alfred L. Stille), is now in the Reynold's Historical Collection of the University of Alabama in Birmingham, Medical Center.

meeting in Toronto. Whether this election was a "last ditch" effort to persuade him to stay at McGill is not known. In any event, his time of departure was imminent. The faculty of Mc-Gill, in a forlorn attempt to keep him, delayed acceptance of his resignation when proffered, but granted him a six months' leave of absence instead. His resignation was finally accepted on October 11, 1884, accompanied by an expression of deepest regret. McGill had lost what Palmer Howard called its "potent ferment."

Before Osler's departure for Philadelphia, he was roundly honored by the faculty and his friends at McGill. Even the students were not to be outdone. They presented him with an engraved hunting-case watch, and as he was leaving they marched in a body to see him off at the railroad station in Montreal.

The news of Osler's appointment brought protests and even indignation from some of the faculty at Pennsylvania, but Osler's graciousness, sincerity, and poise quickly smoothed the troubled waters. However, the launching of Osler at the University of Pennsylvania Medical School was not without some difficulties. The students were not at first impressed, and were even a bit disappointed. In the past they had been used to long lectures, brilliantly delivered. Certainly, Pepper was known for his eloquent lectures. But Osler had a halting speech, and his dress and manner were so informal that the students had some difficulty in adjusting to the change. Very soon, however, everyone overlooked these personal characteristics, and Osler gained the respect of all the students, and the affection of many. This was not the result of any undue effort on his part to be popular, but because they recognized his ability, respected his vast knowledge, and accepted the sincerity so obviously apparent in his relationships with others. His clinical lectures were in reality demonstrations of individual signs and symptoms present in the patients. Indeed, it was here that he began introducing the student to ward teaching and bedside instruction. This mode of teaching was new to the Philadelphia school, and it was here that Osler's talents as a teacher were brought to fruition.

The other members of the faculty had large private practices and only made an appearance at the school for their lectures.

Osler, on the other hand, had no practice and was always available to the students. He literally lived on the wards of the hospital "with increasingly enthusiastic students about him." His consultation practice was practically nonexistent. One colleague remarked "Osler was an excellent consultant, but the trouble was that he could so rarely be found when wanted." He habitually prowled in the library of the nearby College of Physicians instead of keeping office hours or seeing private patients. An "important engagement," the excuse he often used, was usually kept with favorite old books on the library shelves. Though hard to find, when located and an appointment made for a consultation, he was scrupulously punctual, and his visits were invariably of comfort and reassurance both to the patient and his physician. Osler's unusual gift of human sympathy and understanding always left a lasting impression.

He had the faculty of inspiring men to do better than their best. He was a prodigious worker and was always ready with a word of encouragement or an offer of assistance to anyone who was working in the wards or clinic; it might be a subject of critical review, or an unusual case to be studied and reported. His keenness for performing autopsies eventually caused some discord with the accredited pathologists of the city.

Prior to his appearance on the scene, original study or research was unknown at the University of Pennsylvania. There were not even facilities available to instigate any such studies. Osler soon remedied this by improvising a clinical laboratory under the hospital amphitheatre, even using his own microscope which had come with his things from McGill. It was to this improvised laboratory that the students and house staff soon began to troop, imbued with new vigor and interest in the delineation of the cause of disease. Here was a new experience for the students who had previously been given generalizations eloquently delivered from a lectern. Even Dr. William Pepper had been converted to Osler's theory of teaching at the patient's bedside, for in an address at the opening exercises of the University of Pennsylvania Medical School in the fall of 1893, he stated that "The broad basis of modern medical education is careful training of the individual student at the bedside and in the laboratory." Osler's sojourn in Philadelphia had not been in vain.

Dr. Sam W. Gross and his charming wife were among the first to call on Osler in his modest lodgings soon after his arrival in Philadelphia. They invited him to dinner at their home the next day. Thus began a close friendship, and nearly every Sunday thereafter, Osler could be found at the Gross' for dinner.

The Philadelphia years were busy years. During these, he admitted "both pen and brain got a great deal of practice in Philadelphia." Many outstanding medical articles were published, and while there another facet of Osler's wide interests was revealed, namely, his keen interest in medical history and his remarkable gift for letters. From this period dates the beginning of a series of addresses and essays of high literary merit. The years passed swiftly while he was engrossed in clinical teaching, laboratory studies, attending meetings, and writing. Unfortunately, his letters to Ned Milburn during this period were also lost. They most certainly could have furnished us with some interesting insight into his life during his stay in Philadelphia.

No doubt Osler experienced a great deal of loneliness and nostalgia for his native Canada. It was the hearing of a song that brought back memories of his friend Ned Milburn and prompted him to write the following letter. The letter is undated, but was probably written about 1884.

> 131 So. 15th St.
> Phila.

Dear Ned,

   Away in the distance I hear a man, with glorious voice,[2] singing "Bonnie Annie Laurie" and by a curious mental process the thoughts of Barrie & Ned Milburn arise. You sang it many a time just twenty years ago when we used to slip out to the bay.[3]

   How are you? How is the poor leg? Let me know. I am getting settled in [a] new home & like the work very much. Prospects [are] good

[2]Ned Milburn had a fine baritone voice and sang for a number of years in the church choir in his home town of Belleville, Ontario.
[3]This reference is to their school days at Barrie in 1864 when after the lights were out the three boys, Osler, Milburn, and Charlie Locke, would slip out of the window and study by moonlight. This was often followed by a midnight swim in the bay.

in time for consultation work. Slow, of course, at first. Shall be in Toronto in August. If you are up let me know at 83 Wellesley St.[4]
   Kind regards to the wife and bairns.

Yours as of old

W. Osler

P.S. I send you my lectures at Coll. Phy[.] London this spring.[5]

In the summer of 1888, through the influence and friendship
of Dr. John S. Billings, who was the Medical Advisor to the
Board of Trustees of Johns Hopkins University in Baltimore,
Maryland, Dr. Osler became interested in the proposed hospital
and medical school at Johns Hopkins, and September 25, 1888, he
was appointed Physician-in-Chief of the Johns Hopkins Hospital.
Before Osler left for Baltimore in the spring of 1889, his good
friend Dr. Samuel Gross was taken ill and died within a short
time. This occurrence resulted after some years in an event of
great personal consequence to William Osler's future life.

As Osler's whole career had been preparatory for his work in
Philadelphia, so were his five years of work there a necessary
period of maturation for the great decade and a half to follow at
Hopkins. He had found in Philadelphia "the stimulus of tradition, of opportunity for teaching and research and the appreciation of both colleagues and students." Osler won the respect of a
thoroughly entrenched faculty there and succeeded in establishing
himself securely with them. Above all, he demonstrated to the
students how medicine should be learned and taught because he
"knew his subject and how to teach what he knew."

---

[4]The Featherstone Oslers had moved to 83 Wellesley Street, Toronto.
[5]Osler, throughout his life, customarily sent Ned a copy of everything he wrote.

# X

# Hopkins

*To blaze a perfectly new road, untrammelled by tradition, vested interests, or medical "deadwood" — what more could the heart of man desire?\**

When the Johns Hopkins Hospital was opened in 1889, Osler became the first head of the Department of Medicine. With his call to this institution came his great opportunity for excellence in clinical medicine as well as for the advancement of medical education. It was in this setting that he began the most productive and fruitful period in his remarkable career.

William Osler had long cherished an ambition to establish a clinic in which he could put into effect some of his ideas in the teaching as well as in the practice of medicine. Here in Baltimore a model medical clinic was established where medical students were not only allowed, but were encouraged to work in the clinical wards. There young physicians were trained for careers in clinical medicine while medical knowledge also advanced by investigation. Indeed, the accomplishments of Osler and his colleagues during this period were forever woven into the fabric of modern American medicine. During this period he became a speaker and writer of renown. He furthered the cause of sanitation and encouraged the organization of medical societies and libraries. Few men, if any, have enjoyed such a remarkable degree of personal friendship, and the generous admiration of physicians everywhere.

William Osler and Grace Revere Gross (Mrs. Samuel W.), the widow of his old Philadelphia friend, were married quietly in

---

*Lafleur, H. A.: "Early Days at the Johns Hopkins Hospital with Dr. Osler," *Osler Memorial Number,* Inter Ass of Med Museums, Abbott, M. E., Montreal, 1927, p. 270.

Philadelphia May 7, 1892. William was 42 and Grace was 37 years of age at the time. William was most fortunate in his choice of a wife, as from the day of their marriage Grace Osler expanded rather than reduced the radius of Osler's freedom. He brought home droves of friends, students, doctors, and relations, and after briefly greeting the guests he frequently retired to his study to work. His wife graciously continued, uninterrupted, the entertainment of the visitors.[1] For fourteen years in Baltimore, No. 1 West Franklin Street, the Oslers' home, was famous for its hospitality and saw a succession of notable visitors "whose bare enumeration would read like a hotel register."[2]

> 1. West Franklin St.,
> Baltimore.
> 2, 21 [1896]

Dear Ned

I was very glad to have your photograph—you look as natural as ever, & not much older. We are both getting on towards the half century[.][3] I am pegging away as usual, very happy in my professional & college work. Mrs[.] Osler had a small boy about 8 weeks ago which is a comfort. Our other baby died when a week old. This one look[s] durable.[4]

I suppose your chicks are growing up fast. I hear of you occasionally from doctors & patients[.] I wish you could take a trip southwards & stay a week or two with me. I send you a couple of papers which may be of interest[.]

> Your old friend
> Wm. Osler

---

[1]Cushing, vol. I, p. 407. His cordiality is reflected in his letters, where he frequently added a postscript "hope you will be able to pay a nice long visit," or "the kettle boils daily at 4:30," or merely that there was always an extra place at the table at seven o'clock.

[2]*Ibid.*, vol. I, p. 406. The Oslers became so well known in Baltimore by their frequent visitors that the cabbies and railroad station porters knew the arriving passengers by their attire. "Fur caps and square hats to Dr. Osler's," or "A'll take yo' right to Wes' Franklin Street, Sah!"

[3]Osler was 47 years of age.

[4]The birth of a son on December 28, 1895, to William and Grace Osler was a comfort and a source of great happiness. Two years before a baby boy, Paul Revere Osler, had been born, but died when one week old. The new baby was named Edward Revere for Mrs. Osler's brother, to whom she was particularly attached. Mrs. Osler at first was very anxious to name the baby Palmer Howard; Osler insisted on using the name Revere.

FIGURE 11. Edward (Ned) Fairfax Milburn, June 1896. (Courtesy of Miss Grace Evans of Toronto.)

Osler, who had assiduously avoided the private practice of medicine, found himself literally besieged by patients soon after he arrived at Hopkins. This deluge of patients was to continue throughout his days in Baltimore.

Evidently Ned, respecting Osler's now renowned clinical ability, referred to him one of his neighbors and friends, as the following letter suggests:

Dr. William Osler,     Baltimore,
No. 1 W. Franklin Street.    Feb. 21st, 1899.
Consultation Hours,
2.30-4.30 P.M.

Dear Ned:-

Why of course I shall be only too delighted to see Mr. Benjamin, and do anything in my power for him. I will write and let you know about him after the examination.

I hope you are keeping well. I haven't been your way for a long time. I get to Toronto two or three times a year, but indeed I have never been in Belleville. Hoping that some time soon we may meet.

Very sincerely yours,
W. Osler

Love to your family all.

Mr. Benjamin was apparently seen by Osler, and a "rest cure" recommended, as the following letter indicates:

1 West Franklin St,
Baltimore, Md.
Feb. 27th, 1899.

Dear Ned:-

Benjamin stayed her[e] three or four days, and we overhauled his stomach thoroughly. I think that the persistent pain is due altogether to what is known as hyperacidity, and that he has no actual organic disease. He looked badly, was anaemic, and had lost in weight, but I hope that a month at Atlantic City will put him all to rights.

I was glad to hear of you all through him.

Sincerely yours,
Wm. Osler

During the summer of 1904 the Oslers had secured a cottage at Pointe-A'-Pic on Murray Bay in the Province of Quebec, Canada, for a vacation. It was here that Osler spent a few days with his family, and also visited the Revere in-laws, but many of his leisure hours were used in answering accumulated correspondence. It was during this respite and after discussion with Mrs. Osler that he resolved to accept the Regius Professorship of Medicine at Oxford.

FIGURE 12. William Osler and son, Edward Revere, during the Baltimore period. (From Cushing papers in Osler Library at McGill University.)

PL
Pointe a' pic
9th [September 1904]

Dear Ned:

I was on the point of writing to you when your letter came. Mrs. Heineman has told me of your sorrow & trouble about your son[5] — how

---

[5]Edward Milburn was Ned's only son, 24 years old at this time, married and employed as a bank clerk. The diagnosis of tuberculosis was a staggering blow,

terribly sad for you all. And your account is not very satisfactory. Though the early cases with hemorrhages often start very badly & later the disease is arrested. I hope you are keeping him in the "open" on these fine days.[6] While he has fever he should be flat on his back, but the *autumns* out of door life seems so good for the digestion & for the fever. Who is your doctor? Why not let him write me a description of the case? I might be able to be of help.

I do not leave until next Spring[.][7] It will give me a change. I much need a quieter life. Do let me hear how the boy gets on. I shall be in Baltimore on the 24th.

Sincerely yours
Wm Osler

This letter is the first written by Osler to Ned Milburn after learning about the illness of his son through a mutual friend and patient, a Mrs. Heineman. It was obvious that Edward Milburn was suffering from tuberculosis, and Osler knew that the young man was very ill. A hemorrhage early in this disease usually presaged an ominous prognosis. Throughout the short period of Edward's illness Osler was apprehensive concerning the outcome, as was reflected in the tone of his letters. However, he continued to offer helpful suggestions and reassurance as best he could to his old friend Ned.

13 - ix 04
Pointe a' pic
PL.

Dear Ned.

Dr. Sprague[']s account is not very satisfactory — tho, no judgment can be given at so early a stage while he still suffers so from the loss of blood. I have urged a rigid out of door plan of treatment. He may

---

as the disease most commonly progressed unremittingly to death. Then, too, the knowledge that it was contagious was now known; indeed, whole families died as a result of the disease.

[6]The "open air" treatment of tuberculosis to which Osler refers had been introduced earlier in Germany and made popular in the United States by Dr. Trudeau, who was a friend and colleague of Osler's. Osler had been very active in the campaign for the prevention of tuberculosis in the United States and served on several committees that eventually resulted in the organization of a National Society to combat the disease. After he went to England, he was instrumental in organizing the fight there to rid that country of this dread malady.

[7]Osler first mentions his anticipated move to Oxford, a move he hoped would afford him more leisure for his studies and writing.

FIGURE 13. Edward George Milburn, son of Ned Milburn shortly before his fatal illness. (Courtesy of Miss Ruby Milburn.)

object at first. The difficulty is to arrange it satisfactorily in a private house, but many cases do so well, even at home, that it is worth the trial. After the fever subsides & his blood condition improves he might be able to get away to some more suitable climate. The danger is lest it is one of these very acute forms, which often set in with severe hemorrhages. I have asked Dr. Sprague to let me know how he gets on. Do urge upon the lad the importance of giving the open-air treatment a full trial.

Let me hear how he gets along. Mrs. Heineman looks & seems very well[.]

Sincerely yours<br>Wm Osler

Apparently Dr. Sprague's letter telling of young Milburn's illness further alarmed Osler. He was disturbed by the report and the apparent seriousness of the young man's condition. The continued fever and loss of blood were unfavorable signs.

About two weeks later he had word that the patient showed some improvement, although, unfortunately, this improved condition was short lived.

Consultation by Appointment Only
    From 2.30 to 4.30 P.M.
Dr. William Osler<br>No. 1 Franklin Street, West

Baltimore, Sept. 17th. 1904.

Dear Ned,

Glad to hear that the poor laddie is better. Tell the doctor not to hesitate to give enough morphia at night to keep his cough under control. Possibly the inhalation of the creosote would help it.[8] The form of inhaler which you mention seems excellent. Poor boy, he seems to be in a bad way. I am sorry for you all. Please let me hear how he gets on from time to time.

Sincerely yours,<br>Wm Osler

1, West Franklin Street.
Balitmore, Md. Oct. 5th. 1904.

Dear Ned,

It is a very difficult thing to check the fever in tuberculosis. The

---

[8] The treatment of tuberculosis at this time was purely empirical; no specific therapy was known. Control of the persistent cough and fever was often difficult. Many patients had a fulminant form of this disease and died soon after the diagnosis was established.

cool spongings are, I think, less exhausting than the use of the power-
ful, depressing medicines, such as anti-pyrine, etc. Tell the doctor not
to hesitate to give him enough morphia to keep him comfortable at
night as it helps, too, in reducing the fever. It is terribly sad for you
all. I wish I could do something more for you.

> Sincerely yours,
> W Osler

In all of the letters which Osler wrote to Milburn during the
illness of his son, Edward, run the threads of helpful advice, cheerfulness and hope. These traits reveal the character of a man in
whom the face of reality and the soul of compassion were perfectly
blended. It was as if Osler were saying, "I am thinking of you,
concerned for you in your troubles and I am here." And surely it
is this thought that brings strength and comfort to those in distress
— just to know that there is someone who cares.

> 1, West Franklin Street.
> Baltimore, Md. Oct. 11th. 1904.

Dear Ned:-

There is no risk whatever. Scrupulous care must be taken of the
sputum. He should be careful, always, to cough into a handkerchief
or into a towel.

I should be glad to hear from Dr. Sprague about him. What a sad
time it must be for you all. Let me hear, please, from time to time
how he is.

> Sincerely yours,
> W Osler

The mode of transmission of the causative agent of tuberculosis was just beginning to be fully appreciated, and apparently
Milburn was concerned for the rest of his family. Therefore,
Osler, in his letter of October 11th, detailed the precaution that
must be taken to prevent spread of the infection.

Osler's sincere concern is reflected by the increased frequency
of his letters to his old chum, Milburn. Hardly a week passed
without the dispatch of a letter to Milburn. But, as Osler had
surmised, the disease was in its most virulent form and young
Milburn died about two months later.

1, West Franklin Street.
XI. 4. 04

Dear Ned,

How heartbreaking to part from your dear boy — & an only son! I feared all along from the symptoms that it was one of those acute types for which there is rarely any hope. Better so perhaps than a slow lingering two or three years — illness with all its illusive hopes & anxious dreads. Do give my love & heartfelt sympathy to your wife & the girls. They will be inconsolable, poor things!

Affectionately yours
Wm Osler

This letter to Milburn on the loss of his son reveals that Osler had been aware of the seriousness of the illness from the information contained in Milburn's distraught letters. His comment on the heartbreaking loss of "an only son" is all the more poignant in the light of the fact that in years to come Osler, too, would realize such a tragic loss. Osler's interest in the families of his friends is revealed most tellingly in this letter in his sympathetic message to Mrs. Milburn and the girls.

1, West Franklin Street.
XII. 31. 04

Dear Ned,[9]

You must have had a very sad Xmas — with your poor boy away. I wish I could have seen you while I was in Toronto this week, but I was up to my ears in engagements.[10] We do not leave until May. I shall be in Toronto in April. I wish we could all meet then[.]

With love to all at home & best wishes for the New Year.

Ever yours
W Osler

Although overwhelmed with correspondence, teaching and consultations, Osler continued to think of his old friend, Milburn. Particularly on the Christmas so soon after the death of his son,

---

[9]Cushing, vol. I, p. 663.

[10]Osler had visited his family in Canada during the last few days of December 1904. He had officiated at the opening of the Ontario Medical Library Association in Toronto on December 29, 1904, which he had been instrumental in founding. On December 30, 1904, he was honored at a luncheon by the Canadian Club at which he gave an address on "The Anglo-American Relations of Canada."

Milburn was remembered by a note from Osler with words of understanding and good wishes for the New Year and the hope that they might meet in Toronto before his departure for England. Unfortunately, there is no record that the hoped-for visit ever took place.

# XI

# Osler Leaves Hopkins

*. . .he will find it hard to say adieu.*

Osler had had sixteen wonderful years at Johns Hopkins. He had been exceedingly happy there. At Hopkins Osler had been given the opportunity of establishing the kind of teaching service he desired. All of his experience and the ideas he had about how medicine should be taught were put into effect with such success that it brought forth an outpouring of world-wide acclaim for the school. He had been able to complete his textbook *The Principles and Practices of Medicine,* and had continued prodigiously to produce medical observations and submit scientific papers to the best journals.

But with this world-wide fame came an ever increasing demand on his time from medical organizations and consultation practice. He became known as "the doctors' doctor," and almost every day there was either a physician as a patient, or a member of his family in the consultation room to see Dr. Osler. He had long since been forced to curtail some of his burgeoning consultation practice, but to turn away a physician or a member of his family was difficult to do.

In the spring of 1904 both he and his wife became concerned with his ever increasing work load. It was at this juncture that a letter from his old friend, Sir J. Burdon-Sanderson,[1] the Regius Professor at Oxford, arrived inquiring if he might be interested in an appointment to the Oxford position, as Burdon-Sanderson planned to retire at the end of the year due to ill health. There

---

*From Mrs. Osler's letter as quoted in Cushing: *Life of Sir William Osler.* vol. I, p. 654.

[1]Sir John Burdon-Sanderson, 1828-1905, Waynflete Professor of Physiology, 1882-1895, Regius Professor of Medicine, Oxford, 1895-1905.

FIGURE 14. Edward Revere Osler, circa 1905. (From Cushing papers in Library at McGill University.)

remains some mystery as to who had mentioned Osler's name for this position, but his name had been suggested to Sanderson, and he immediately contacted Osler.

Somewhat of a dichotomous philosophy had arisen as to the type of man who should fill the Regius Chair at Oxford. This was a crown appointment and did not have to meet with approval of the University authorities. However, the medical faculty at Oxford felt that a man from one of the basic science disciplines should be appointed, whereas the alumni were equally adamant that a clinician should be selected in order to better coordinate the school with the clinical years. For some time most of the clinical training had been given in the London hospitals. The professorship carried a stipend of only £400 yearly, and it was immediately deemed pertinent to inquire as to where they could obtain a distinguished clinician who would be willing to give up his practice for such a small income.

Osler obviously was an ideal choice. He was widely known, not only as a clinician who had done substantial original fundamental research, but an accomplished classical scholar. He, most certainly, would fit well into the literary society at Oxford.

Mrs. Osler, when told of Sanderson's inquiry, wrote, "as I read the letter I felt a tremendous weight lifted from my shoulders as I had become very anxious about the danger of his (Osler's) keeping on at the pace he had been going for several years in Baltimore."[2] In fact, however, when offered the position, Osler still was reluctant to accept. When Mrs. Osler was appraised of his indecision she wired him, "Do not procrastinate — accept at once."

Osler accepted the position, but on writing Sanderson revealed some reluctance on leaving Baltimore: "while very happy here and with splendid facilities, probably unequalled in English-speaking countries, I am overworked and find it increasingly hard to serve the public and carry on my teaching."[3] He felt that the position at Oxford, however, would afford him the time needed

---

[2]Cushing, vol. I, p. 644.
[3]Cushing, vol. I, p. 644.

for his writing, which he so loved to do. Oxford brought, at least originally, the two things Osler desired most, leisure and opportunity for study.

Osler, in explaining his decision, insisted that the post at Oxford was chiefly ornamental, though he had hopes of making it more useful, and he did exactly this. The Regius Professorship acquired more prestige and luster during his tenure.

During the months before leaving for England, Osler was in demand on every side. On February 22, 1905, in connection with anniversary ceremonies at Hopkins, Osler was asked to speak, and he took this occasion to give his farewell address. He had prepared a now-famous essay entitled "The Fixed Period." The day was marked by an outpouring of appreciation for Osler and sincere regrets at his departure.

His address was most timely, and well thought out. The main theme concerned the fact that historically most human achievements occur between the ages of twenty-five and forty. Osler, now fifty-five years of age, was obviously justifying his departure, i.e. making room for a younger investigator who was still in the "green" years of accomplishments. Unfortunately, the press, possibly bored with the usual routine stories and needled by his frequent rebuffs to their inquiry, hit upon one statement of his address. He was quoting from the little-known novel *The Fixed Period* by Anthony Trollope, who had whimsically used a plot that hinged upon the scheme of a fictional college where men retired at 60 years of age for a year of contemplation before peaceful departure by chloroform!

The newspapers latched upon this statement and headlined the story throughout the country: OSLER RECOMMENDS CHLOROFORM AT SIXTY. The uproar continued for days and weeks with mounting satirical criticism of Osler.

Usually Osler was completely undaunted by adverse criticism and never acknowledged it or attempted any defense. Although he flatly refused to alter or confirm the press' criticism of his quote, which was widely used out of context, he did append a preface to the second edition of his "Aequanimitas" in which he made his peace with the world but reemphasized his original idea.[4]

He referred to the furor in a letter to Milburn dated February 28, 1905, with the lightheartedness so characteristic of his personality. It is sure, however, that this incident must have saddened him on his departure from Hopkins.

> 1, West Franklin Street.
> Baltimore, Md. Feb. 28th, 1905.
>
> Dear Ned:-
>
> I will let you know when I hope to be in Toronto. It is somewhat uncertain at present. The newspapers have taken my chloroform joke altogether too seriously.[5] I am surprised and mortified at it. I thought there was a greater sense of humour in the community.
>
> Give my love to your wife and daughters,
>
> > Ever yours,
> > W Osler

Of the incident, Osler wrote in a letter to a friend, "Such a torrent of abuse and misunderstanding began to flow in that I took my old master, Plato's advice, and crept under the shelter of a wall until the storm blew over."[6]

---

[4]Osler wrote "To this edition I have added the three valedictory addresses delivered before leaving America. One of these, 'The Fixed Period,' demands a word of explanation. 'To interpose a little ease,' to relieve a situation of singular sadness on parting from my dear colleagues of the Johns Hopkins University, I jokingly suggested for the relief of a senile professoriate an extension of Anthony Trollope's plan mentioned in his novel *The Fixed Period*. To one who had all his life been devoted to older men, it was not a little distressing to be placarded in a worldwide way as their sworn enemy, and to every man over sixty whose spirit I may have thus unwittingly bruised, I tender my heartfelt regrets. Let me add, however, that the discussion which followed my remarks has not changed, but has strengthened my belief that the real work of life is done before the fortieth year and that after the sixtieth year it would be best for the world and best for ourselves if men rested from their labours."

[5]Newspaper clipping about "chloroform joke" was attached.

[6]Osler was always wary of the newspapers. In Dr. W. B. Bean's *Aphorisms* he is quoted as saying: "In the life of every successful physician there comes the temptation to toy with the Delilah of the press — daily or otherwise. There are times when she may be courted with satisfaction, but beware! Sooner or later she is sure to play the harlot, and has left many a man shorn of his strength, namely the confidence of his professional brethren."

On re-reading the speech now after more than half a century, it is difficult to comprehend how such a misunderstanding could have occurred. The address reads today with the brilliance and satisfaction that it was intended over a half century ago. The fatuous newspaper reports of that day seem dull and out of context with the central idea of the momentous address.

Osler made a brief visit to see his mother in Toronto before leaving for England, but the time was too short to meet with his friend Ned.

> 1, West Franklin Street.
> Baltimore, Md., Apr. 18, 1905.
>
> Dear Ned:-
>
> I was only in Toronto for Sunday, so that I did not think it worth while to telegraph you. I hope to be out here in January and February to spend some time in Canada, and I hope to see you then. We leave on the 18th of May. My address will be just Oxford.
>
> With love to your wife and the girls,
>
> Sincerely yours,
> W Osler

On May 2, 1905, a farewell dinner for Dr. Osler was held at the Waldorf-Astoria Hotel in New York City. Represented at this dinner were the leaders of the medical profession of Canada and the United States. There were some five hundred participants from many sections of the two countries. Osler closed his farewell talk with a reference to his ideals[7]

> I have had three personal ideals: One to do the day's work well and not to bother about tomorrow. You may say that is not a satisfactory ideal. It is: and there is not one which the student can carry with him into practice with greater effect. To it more than anything else, I owe whatever success I have had to this power of settling down to the day's work and trying to do it well to the best of my ability, and letting the future take care of itself.
>
> The second ideal has been to act the golden rule, as far as in me lay, toward my professional brethren and toward the patients committed to my care.
>
> And the third has been to cultivate such a measure of equanimity as would enable me to bear success with humility, the affection of my

---

[7]*L 'Envoi, in Aequanimitas,* 2nd ed. Philadelphia, Blakiston, 1906.

friends without pride, and to be ready when the day of sorrow and grief comes to meet it with courage befitting a man.

Apparently in the rush of his departure from the United States and Canada he was unable to see Ned. He had a number of meetings and several farewell banquets to attend. He wrote in his notebook that he sailed from New York on the *S.S. Cedric* on May 19th "almost dead." He arrived in Oxford on May 27, 1905, and immediately took up residence in Professor Max Mueller's home, which he had rented completely furnished.

There in Oxford, where he had fled from overwork, he naïvely thought he could lead a quiet life of leisure, but a man with Osler's vitality, reputation, and widespread interests was not destined for a period of semi-retirement. Soon he was completely immersed in reorganizing the scope of the Regius Professorship, and in addition promptly became involved in a number of scientific endeavors.

# XII

## Oxford

*O strong of soul by what shore*
*Tarriest thou now? For that force,*
*Surely has not been left vain.*
*Somewhere, surely, afar,*
*In the sounding labour — house vast*
*Of being, is practiced that strength*
*Zealous, beneficent, firm!**

Oxford with its ancient colleges, libraries, and intellectual atmosphere, was an ideal choice for Osler to spend his remaining years. There, he could relax from the constant press of work; and there also he could have time for the pursuit and enjoyment of his literary interests. The Regius professorship was more an honorary position than a working one, with the principal duties being several lectures a year and participation in the examinations of prospective graduates. However, as it happened, his life was not too quiet, and the spirit of work that was in him kept him quite active. "He adapted himself from the first as though born an Oxonian and took the keenest interest in every detail of the new life."[1] Indeed, Oxford was to become "the center from which he and his activities radiated far beyond the geographical boundaries of England."[2]

> 7, Norham Gardens,[3]
> Oxford.
> June 13, 1905.

Dear Ned:-

    Yes, I only had a day in Toronto and was half dead trying to see

---

*Matthew Arnold, "Rugby Chapel."
[1]Cushing. Vol. II, p. 28.
[2]Rolleston, Sir Humphrey: Bull. IX, Inter Ass of Med Museums, *Osler Memorial Number*, Abbott, M. E. (Ed.), Montreal, 1927, p. 349.
[3]The Max Muller home at 7 Norham Gardens, Oxford, was obtained for the Oslers' temporary abode.

FIGURE 15. An Osler family portrait taken at 13 Norham Gardens, Oxford. (From Cushing papers in Osler Library at McGill University.)

all my relatives and friends.[4] I am reprinting my farewell address. I hope it will be out in October, when I will send you a copy. We got here two weeks ago and are very comfortably settled.[5] Everything is, of course, very different, but I think I shall settle down into a quiet academic life.

    With love to all at home,

Sincerely yours,
W Osler

The setting was perfect for the tranquil life Osler needed and thought he desired, but his reputation and love of activity were to make his solitude short-lived. After only a few weeks he began to accept invitations, visited the Regius Professor at Cambridge, sat for his portrait by Sargent, and began to receive an ever swelling tide of visitors and friends who came to his home in Oxford. Originally, however, Osler did decline some pressing speaking engagements, stating that "mentally, too, I am rather desiccated, having had a most trying year."

It was not long after the Oslers' advent at Oxford that his professional and social activities again began to reach an incredible rate, obviating any relief of mental and physical strain that he had hoped would result from his move from Baltimore. In a letter dated July 17, 1906, he complained that he had been asked to be a member of the Royal Commission on Vivisection, but he was reluctant to get tied up "with these outside things. Already they have been piling up and they take the leisure I need for all sorts of work."[6]

7, Norham Gardens,
Oxford.
November 11th. 1905.

Dear Ned:-

    My address has only just been printed over here.[7] I am sending you a copy to-day.

---

[4]Osler paid a brief visit to Toronto, principally to see his mother prior to his departure for England. Again, due to press of duties, he was unable to see Ned on this visit.

[5]The Oslers arrived in Oxford late in May, 1905. In a letter to her mother, Mrs. Osler states, "we found everything ready — butler at the door, maids in the bedrooms, and ready, a delicious dinner." Cushing, vol. II, p. 82.

[6]Cushing, vol. II, p. 55.

I have settled down into a quiet life here and like it very much. We are finding some difficulty in getting a suitable house, but I think we shall like everything here very much. Of course, the life is very different, but very restful after the sort of racket I have had for some years.

I am very sorry to hear of your brother['s illness].[8] It is such a serious affection. You must have been terribly distressed about it.

Give my love to all at home.

Sincerely yours,<br>W Osler

In December 1906, William, Grace, and Revere joined the Osler clan in Canada for the celebration of his mother Ellen's one-hundredth birthday. The birthday cake was so large that it required the services of two men to carry it, and had five layers, representing the five reigns of her century — George III and IV, William, Victoria, and Edward VII. Due to her age and infirmities, Ellen Osler was not allowed to leave her room at her Wellesley Street home.[9]

|  |  |  | Sunday |
|---|---|---|---|
| Dec 16th |  | Craigleigh, |  |
| 1906 | AM | Rosedale. |  |

Dear Ned

Mother thanks you so much for your kind thought. She remembers you as one of my old friends. She keeps wonderfully well — & is bright mentally. I wish I could see you, but it is impossible to stop over in Belleville this time. We have to be in Boston for Xmas. I wish you could arrange some time to come over for a few weeks. You would enjoy Oxford so much. I am sending you my Harveian Oration.[10] Did

---

[7]Probably "Unity, Peace, and Concord: a farewell address to the Medical Profession of the United States," Oxford, H. Hart, 1905, p. 22.

[8]Again, Osler shows his affectionate concern for his friend. Milburn's brother had lockjaw (tetanus).

[9]After Canon Osler's retirement, he and his wife moved to Toronto. The Reverend Featherstone Osler died in 1895, at the age of ninety.

[10]"The Growth of Truth as Illustrated in the Discovery of the Circulation of the Blood" was presented to the Royal College of Physicians October 18, 1906, and printed in the *British Medical Journal* as well as the *Lancet*. The Harveian Oration is considered to be the most prestigeous event in British medicine. It was made possible by a perpetuating gift from William Harvey in 1651 and since that time has been given annually almost without interruption.

I send you Counsels & Ideals — which one of my students pulled out from my writings![11] Send me a line to c/o Mrs[.] Revere[,] Canton[,] Mass.[12]

Love to all yours,<br>
Sincerely yours<br>
Wm Osler

While in Toronto, the William Oslers apparently were guests at Craigleigh, the home of Sir Edmund Boyd Osler, one of William's elder brothers who had been very successful in business. The house stood in the center of a thirteen acre estate bordering the Rosedale ravine in the old portion of Toronto. It was large and comfortable and had three bathrooms! On the spacious grounds were two neat brick homes, one for the head gardener and the other allotted to the family of a deceased coachman. A larger house on the corner of the property belonged to an uncle and aunt (perhaps Francis Gordon, as he was in the Toronto office of Osler and Hammond). Edmund lived the life of an English country squire, reveling in his gardens and his grandchildren. Several months after Edmund's death the house was demolished to make way for civic improvements in the city.

Osler and his family landed in New York City on December 6th, 1906, and first visited friends in Baltimore. He went from there to Hamilton, Ontario, and visited briefly with his friends Drs. Archibald Malloch and John Mullins.

While in Canada he was tendered the presidency of the University of Toronto which he declined after an appropriate interval. He returned to Boston by way of Montreal where he had a brief visit with friends. The Oslers then joined the Revere clan for Christmas in Canton, Massachusetts. Immediately after the holiday festivities he journeyed again to Baltimore for a brief visit with Dr. H. B. Jacobs. The Oslers returned to Oxford in January, sailing from New York on January 8th, 1907.

---

[11]Camac, C. N. B.: *Counsels and Ideals, from the Writings of William Osler.* Boston and New York, Houghton, 1905. This was a compilation of excerpts from Osler's writings compiled by one of his former students with the approval of Osler.

[12]There is no record that Milburn replied.

FIGURE 16. The Osler home in Oxford, England: 13, Norham Gardens. (From Cushing papers in Osler Library at McGill University.)

Feb 1st [1907]
13 Norham Gardens
Oxford

Dear Ned,

I am sending *Counsels & Ideals* and the Harveian Oration. I did send my collection of addresses-Aequanimitas[13] — did I not. We had a very good passage back & we are now trying to get settled in our own house.[14]

        Love to the family.

          Yours ever.

          W.O.

The Oslers' Oxford home became known as "The Open Arms," reflecting its warm hospitality to an unending stream of

---

[13]*Aequanimitas, with Other Addresses to Medical Students, Nurses, and Practitioners of Medicine*. Philadelphia, Blakiston, 1906.

[14]13 Norham Gardens, Oxford. This was the Oslers' home until Mrs. Osler died on August 31, 1928. She left the home in perpetuity for the Regius Professor of Medicine at Oxford. Sometime in April, 1906, Osler purchased this home. They moved in August of that year, but the remodeling was not completed until early spring 1907.

visitors. "Race, nationality, profession, creed mattered little, so wide and catholic was the warm-hearted hospitality there."[15] Invitations to visit him at his Oxford home went out steadily in short notes from Osler, and most were probably accepted. It was not uncommon for one of his letters written after a recent holiday to begin "We had a very strenuous New Year — seven in the house over Sunday — such a jolly party."

> 13, Norham Gardens,
> Oxford.
> March 26th. 1907.

Dear Ned:-

I am surprised that you have not received a copy of my address.[16] I will write about it at once to the publisher.

The shaking you speak of seems to be rather of the nature of writer's cramp causing the pen to stick.[17] It might be well every night to bathe the hand in very hot water and then rub the fingers thoroughly and the spaces between the bones at the back of the hand where the interossoei are, with sweet oil. I do not think it is anything about which you need be specially anxious.

You will have noticed about my mother's death.[18] It was very unexpected. She had been surprisingly well.

Love to all at home,

> Sincerely yours,
> W Osler

P.S. Have I sent you a recent photograph?

Ellen Osler's influence on the fame and fortune of her family was considerable. In her quiet manner, she was a source of strength for her children, and they continued to do her honor "all the days of her life."

---

[15]Cushing, vol. II, p. 103.

[16]Apparently the Harveian Oration.

[17]In the letters of Milburn to Cushing after Osler's death, Milburn's handwriting shows the tremulous irregularity seen in aging individuals. It seems highly unlikely that this condition would have begun as early as 1907. Although Osler showed a sympathetic concern, he stopped short of giving his friend Ned absolute encouragement about complete recovery.

[18]Ellen Picton Osler died March 18, 1907, and William attributed her demise to anxiety over his brother Edward's illness. Edward, who had gout, had made his home with his mother. Two months later Edward also died.

From the Regius Professor of Medicine, Oxford.
        13 Norham Gardens
         October 7th. [1907]

Dear Ned,

    I send on a book to-day, you will be interested in it, particularly in Kipling's poems.[19] It is a book that would be worth introducing into the schools in Canada.

    That was indeed a great turn-over, and it will do good. Love to Mrs[.] Milburn and the girls.

                     Yours
                     W. Osler


In October 1908, with his textbook revision completed,[20] he and Mrs. Osler spent the winter in Paris for what he termed a "brain-dusting."

He spent many hours browsing in the Bibliotheque Nationale and the Bibliotheque de L' Ecole de Medicine and others. The following letter was written during his sojourn in Paris.

                     Paris
                     4th Jan
                      /09

Dear Ned[21]

    It was nice to have the Xmas reminder from you. Did you get my volume of essays — The Alabama student?[22] I ordered a copy to be sent about the end of November. I am taking a winter off for some special work on the continent. I have been here for 3 months working in the Hospitals[.] We go on to Italy next week. I hope to be out in Canada in June. I must arrange to see you. It would be such a pleasure. I hope you are all keeping well. Do you ever hear from Jemmy Morgan?[23] I have heard nothing of him for years[.] I often think of the happy days we had as boys. Are any of the Checkleys alive? What

---

[19]Fletcher, C. R. L. and Kipling, R.: *History of England.* New York, Doubleday, 1907.

[20]The seventh edition of Osler's textbook, *Principles and Practice of Medicine,* which was published in 1909.

[21]Quoted in Cushing, vol. II, p. 150.

[22]*An Alabama Student, and Other Biographical Essays,* Oxford U. P., 1908.

[23]James Chapin Morgan was Superintendent of Education for Simcoe County, Ontario, for 36 years. Afterwards he returned to Oakville, circa 1899, as Superintendent of Forester's Orphan House and served as president of the first Boy Scout Council there.

a good [time] we had that winter! How far you could throw stones
on the ice! I suppose you still have muscles like iron. I kept [sic]
pretty well — not quite the energy of some years ago but I have much
to interest me in my new life at Oxford. How I wish I could go with
you for a row on the Thames. My boy at 13 (now with us for Xmas)
pulls an excellent oar.[24] Dear me how your heart must ache for your
boy.

    My address will be Oxford. Letters will be forwarded

Your affec friend<br>Wm Osler

Osler sailed for America on April 21st, 1909, for one of his
overly crowded visits and lecture tours. He had planned to leave
on April 14th, 1909, but his frequently recurring bronchitis delayed him. On arrival, he went first to Baltimore and spoke to the
Hopkins Historical Club on the life of Michael Servetus. He went
from there to Washington, D. C., to visit friends, but was back in
Baltimore for the dedication of the new building of the Maryland
Medical and Chirurgical Faculty, with which Osler's encouragement had much to do. He later visited Harvard University and
then stopped briefly at Buffalo, N. Y., before proceeding on to
Toronto, where he made his brother Edmund's home, "Craigleigh," his headquarters.

Monday<br>80, Crescent Road,<br>Toronto.<br>[June 7, 1909]

Dear Ned

    I will stop over to see you on Thursday, leaving here by the 9:30
train G.T.R. I will go on to Montreal by a later train. I will let you
know should I have to change my plans on the day[.] It will be a
great pleasure to see you again[.]

Sincerely yours<br>Wm Osler

It was from "Craigleigh" that Osler wrote Ned the preceding
note. The visit was a brief one, possibly just overnight or for only
a few hours. This was the first time he had seen Milburn since he
left Canada, and it may even have been the first since the days at

---

[24]Revere joined them in Paris for the Christmas vacation 1908.

Trinity College in Toronto. It was also his first to Milburn's home at Belleville.

13, Norham Gardens,
Oxford.
June 18th, 10.

Dear Ned,

I have been away on the Continent, hence the delay in replying to yours of the 18th of May.[25] I am writing to your daughter today C.O. Dr. Lees Hospital, giving her a couple of letters of introduction and my congratulations on finishing her course.[26] I have asked her to write and let me know her plans and prospects. I could give her letters to any of the large cities that would help her make a good start.

The boy is at Winchester enjoying it very much; he is not a student, but is taking to natural history as much as I did.[27]

We are sailing for Canada towards the end of the summer and shall call and see you again.

Love to Mrs. Milburn and the girls.

Ever yours,
Wm Osler

13, Norham Gardens,
Oxford.
July 27th, 10.

Dear Ned,

We are sailing on Saturday by the Empress of Ireland. I shall have to cut my visit rather short, as I may have to return by way of New York early in September. I will let you know if I can stop over in Belleville, I hope of course to be able to do so.

I have not got a reprint of that article I am sorry to say; I may have them later.

Sincerely yours,
Wm Osler

Osler made his "annual" visit to America in the late summer of 1910. He sailed for Quebec on July 29, 1910, with his wife and Revere. They were accompanied by their guests, Ottilie Wright and Nona Gwyn. These two young ladies from Canada visited in Oxford in the spring of 1910. Cushing comments that their visit

---

[25]The Oslers spent nine months in France and Italy during 1909-10.

[26]Milburn's daughter, Nonie, was a trained nurse.

[27]Revere Osler entered the famous public school for boys (they were referred to as men) at Winchester in January 1910.

contributed "to the not inconsiderable distraction of the Rhodes Scholars." Miss Nona Gwyn was William Osler's niece, daughter of his sister Chattie, while Miss Ottilie Wright was the daughter of his old McGill schoolmate, Dr. H. P. Wright. He referred to Nona as "plain but very sweet." They went to England to be presented at Court but the sudden death of King Edward VII resulted in cancellation of all social activities. To ameliorate their disappointment, the Oslers took them for a week's "frolic" on the continent. The two young ladies returned to England in the spring of 1911 and were presented at Court during the festivities accompanying the coronation of King George V.

> Tuesday
> The Spinney[28]
> Pointe á Pic
> P.Q.
> [August 9, 1910]
>
> Dear Ned
>      Could you come to Toronto next week — Wednesday the 17th. My time is so short that I cannot stop over in Belleville on my way from Montreal.[29] You must let me send you the railway ticket[.][30] Let me know by which train you arrive & I will meet you. My brother E.B. will give you a bed & we can have a nice evening together[.] I am awfully sorry to be unable to see Mrs Milburn & the girls[.]
>
> Yours affec friend
> Wm Osler

Osler sailed for home as he is reported to have said, "in a swelter," on September 6th, 1910, aboard the liner *Kaiser Wilhelm II* and arrived in Oxford September 13, 1910.

In 1911, Edmund Boyd Osler persuaded Dr. Osler to join his party for a six-week holiday in Egypt, and Osler's letters during this excursion are full of enthusiasm and descriptive detail. In Cairo he visited the famous Khedival Library and the hospital. During the trip up the Nile he saw Denderah and the Temple of

---

[28]The Oslers' vacation place at Murray Bay in Canada.

[29]On the same date he wrote Dr. H. B. Jacobs that he would start his "rounds" next Sunday in Montreal, Belleville, Toronto, and Hamilton.

[30]There is no record that this meeting took place.

Hathor, at which he exclaimed: "Heavens, what feeble pigmies we are — even with steam and electricity and the Panama Canal!"

He sent an enthusiastic post card to Milburn from nearly every stop.

[Card to Edward Milburn, Esq.][31]                              [March 3, '11]

　How are these for Lotus Colums [sic]? These chaps were mighty builders. We are not in the same class.

W.O.

Osler frequently resorted to post cards as a means of "keeping in touch," probably in order to save time. Sir George Savage said of Osler's correspondence, "He was, in some respects rather like Gladstone in that he communicated his wishes or his intentions by means of post cards."

[March 19, 1911]

[Card to Edward Milburn, Esq.][32]

　Le Caire. Temple Chafra Sphinx et Pyramide Cheops. Top notch of human effort! Nothing like these in the world

W.O.

[Card to Edward Milburn, Esq.][33]                              [March 25, '11]

EDFOU

Interieure des Temples

This is the most perfect of the ancient temples — and is a beauty. It is late — in the Ptolemy days but wonderful. It was completely covered by an Egyptian village & took years to dig out.

W.O.

[Card to Edward Milburn, Esq.][34]                              [No date]

Pompei, Casa del Vetti

This gives a good idea of the court or garden of about the best of the Pompei houses. The statues fountains & are all in place. The living rooms open from the court — the walks are beautifully decorated

W.O.

---

[31]In Cushing Archives, Yale University.

[32]In Cushing Archives.

[33]*Ibid.*

[34]*Ibid.*

[March 28, '11]
[Card to Edward Milburn, Esq.][35]                              28.3.11
      SORRENTO — Villa Marion Crawford vista dal Mare
Here is where Crawford wrote most of his works[36] I am on my way
home. We have had a wonderful trip. Love to all at home.
                              W.O.


On his return to London, Osler found the country in happy
expectation of the coronation of King George V. He showed Mrs.
Osler a letter from Number 10 Downing Street, marked confi-
dential. It notified him that his name was on the list of coronation
honors for a baronetcy. Mrs. Osler expostulated, "What excuses
are you going to give for declining it? You have always said you
would." He replied, "I think I'll have to accept — Canada will be
so pleased. There is only one Canadian baronet."

They attempted to keep the news secret, but it leaked out, and
the house was soon besieged by telegraph boys. Congratulatory
telegrams, cables, and letters flooded his Oxford home.

The impressions made upon him are revealed in an extant
letter to his sister:

Dear Chattie:[37]
    You must have had a shock yesterday morning when you saw Bill's
name in the coronation honour list. We had word about ten days ago
from Mr. Asquith, but nothing could be said. I did not know when
it was to come out. I thought not until after the coronation, but
yesterday before I was out of bed the telegrams began to rain in and
there has been a perfect stream — more than 100 from England and
49 cables, U.S. and Canada; 2 from India. Letters galore. Grace was in
town with Mrs. McCagg. Nona and Ottilie had been up at a dance so
we did not let them know until later. I have had rather more than my
share but these court honours mean so much here. And when in the
swim we must take what comes. These things have never bothered me,
and we have had so much, and been so happy, that we really did not
need it as much as some poor fellow who has done more but has not
caught the public eye. I am glad for the family. I wish Father and
Mother had been alive and poor B.B. and Nellie. It is wonderful how

---

[35]In Cushing Archives.

[36]Francis Marion Crawford, American novelist — 1854-1909.

[37]Cushing, vol. II, p. 276.

a bad boy (who could chop off his sister's fingers) may fool his fellows if he once gets to work. Ask Bull Lyon how he accounts for it. The girls are greatly excited. Nona looks so well. Her presentation picture is so good and as for Grace — it was her royal appearance that settled George R. Love to Charley and the girls.

> Your affec bro.
> 'Sir Billy' !!!!

## And to Ned,

From the Regius Professor of Medicine, Oxford.

> July 1st. [1911]

Dear Ned[38]

Thanks for your letter. Every one seems pleased. These things never bothered me[39] — I have had so much more than my share, but in this country they mean much[.] It is nice not to have had to pull wires or worry one's friends. I cannot come out this year. I am very busy trying to get my text-book revised. I hope to be out next spring[.]

Love to the family — I hope you keep well.

> Yours ever,
> W. Osler
> N. Wales,[40]
> Llanddulas
> 4th [September 1911]

Dear Ned[41]

I hope you have all had a good summer. I do not believe I ever answered your kind letter of congratulations. I put it aside with the special ones[.] There were over 1000 letters & telegrams[.] Of course we were greatly pleased. These things go for much over here; tho personally I have never cared much. I have had more than my share [of] a good deal. I do not know how or why I got it. We have had a month here in N Wales in a lovely valley — so fresh and green[.] The

---

[38]Milburn had written a note on this letter stating, "I had written congratulations on his title."

[39]In a letter to a friend Osler states that the bestowing of a title on him was "much to the embarrassment of my democratic simplicity, but it does not seem to make any difference in my internal sensitiveness." (Cushing.)

[40]The Oslers' vacation in the summer of 1911 was spent at Llanddulas, a tiny village in North Wales.

[41]Osler had apparently forgotten that he had replied to a letter from Milburn, congratulating him on his new title. He had diligently set out to acknowledge the flood of congratulatory messages. Many remained unanswered at the time he left on his vacation, so he took them along to answer during his leisure.

Thames valley is burnt brown — 53 days of continuous sunshine — an unheard of thing in England. I am not coming out this year — my holiday in Egypt has to count.[42] I shall get away next year[.] Did you get the Fletcher & Kipling History of England. I thought you would be interested in it. My boy is thriving — bigger than I am now.[43] He is no student, but a good lad and no trouble.

    Love to all at home.

Ever yours,
W.O

FIGURE 17. Sir William Osler and Revere, circa 1911. Osler says: "My boy is thriving — bigger than I am now." (See letter to Ned Milburn dated September 4, 1911.) (From the Cushing papers in Osler Library at McGill University.)

---

[42]The Oslers had to forego their "annual" trip to America in the summer of 1911.
[43]See Figure 17.

From the Regius Professor of Medicine, Oxford.

26th June, 1912.

Dear Ned,

The boy had pneumonia three months ago — a very short and sharp attack from which he recovered very promptly. We are having a very busy summer — so many people coming and going. I was very sorry to hear of your brother Robert's death. We saw Mrs. Campbell here looking very well.[44] My love to you all.

Sincerely yours,
Wm Osler

Early in March 1912, Revere developed pneumonia while in school at Winchester. The Oslers spent some anxious days there, but his recovery was swift. In April the Oslers took him to Northern Italy to a warmer climate. Osler went on to Rome for the VIIth International Tuberculosis Congress, and Revere went back to school.

Osler wrote Milburn many small notes during this period. Indeed, this was characteristic of the voluminous correspondence that he carried on. Cushing says

the length of a man's letters are usually in inverse proportion to the number of his correspondents, and if he would retain his friends, old and new, as Osler did, there should be no wasted words.

In 1911 Osler had been invited to give the Silliman lectures at Yale University. Due to press of duties, he requested a delay of a year in order to prepare the series. The title he chose was *The Evolution of Modern Medicine*. There were six lectures which began on the afternoon of April 21, 1913. They were finally published after Osler's death by the Yale Press in 1921.

Oct. 7. 1912,
13, Norham Gardens,
Oxford.

Dear Ned

You will be wondering what has become of me, but I have had to postpone my lectures until the spring[.] So I shall not see you until May next. I hope you have had a good summer. We went to Scotland where the boy had very good fishing & I had a nice peaceful time. We

---

[44]Osler probably refers to a mutual friend who paid a visit to his home in Oxford.

had too much rain, but that was everywhere. How are you all? I hope
the girls are well. Drop me a line before long.

Yours ever,
Wm Osler

The Oslers spent their vacation at Tongue in the very north-
ernmost part of Sutherlandshire. They were joined by Revere's
friend Raleigh Parkin and his sister Alice. Both Revere and Parkin fished the Locks Craggie and Laoghal as well as in the Kyle of
Tongue. Letters from Osler during this time tell of Revere's
wonderful luck at fishing.

31st [December 1912]

13, Norham Gardens,
Oxford.

Dear Ned

Thanks for the Rabbi Ben Ezra — a favorite poem of mine, the
best of Brownings, I think.[45] I hope you have had a good Xmas. We
had a house full — a daughter of E.B; & her three, H.S. Osler & his
son from Toronto & a sister-in law & two nieces from Boston.[46] My
boy was 17 last week — growing a big fellow, not much at his books but
a very good sort. Thank the lassie for her photograph. — very good.[47]
She must keep the house lively[.] I hope to be out in April & should
be able to stop over at Belleville on my way from Toronto some time
in May[48]

Love to you all

Ever yours
Wm Osler

His trip to America in the spring of 1913 turned out to be a
lecture tour, including Baltimore, Philadelphia, New Haven,
Boston, New York, Toronto, and Montreal. In his notes on his
itinerary he has written, "Monday, May 12, Belleville to see Ned
Milburn." So if all went according to plan, he made another short
visit to his old friend. He arrived back in England on May 23,
1913.

---

[45]Milburn had sent the poem "Rabbi Ben Ezra" by Robert Browning as a Christmas
gift to Osler.
[46]The "Open Arms" was crowded as usual during the festive Christmas season of
1912. The sister-in-law from Boston was probably Mrs. Osler's sister, Mrs. Chapin.
[47]Probably Nonie, a daughter of Ned Milburn.
[48]He refers to his forthcoming trip to America to give the Silliman lectures at Yale.

The year passed, and with the Christmas season went the customary note to his old friend, Ned.

From the Regius Professor of Medicine, Oxford.

12, Dec. 1913.

Dear Ned,

I send you to-day a couple of addresses and I hope by Christmas you will have another which I gave to the Yale students on "A Way of Life."[49]

No I was not in Toronto in October. We have had a very busy term — so much to do. I have not yet finished the revision of my lectures on "The Evolution of Modern Medicine," which I delivered last year at Yale.[50]

The boy is home — just up for his entrance examination.[51]

Love to the family. I hope you will have a very happy Christmas.

Sincerely yours,
Wm Osler

Again after Christmas, Osler sent the following letter:

From the Regius Professor of Medicine, Oxford.

5, Jan. 1914.

Dear Ned,

I am so glad you had a good Christmas. We have had a very busy time. My brother Frank came over from British Columbia with his wife — I had not seen him for thirty years — and Lady Osler's brother from Sydney and a couple of other friends, so that we were very busy.[52]

My Yale lectures on The Evolution of Modern Medicine are in type, but I have not yet had time to finish them. You will have a copy as soon as they are out.

With love to you all at home,

Sincerely yours,
Wm Osler/
W.H.E.

---

[49]"A Way of Life," a now famous lay sermon given to Yale students Sunday evening, April 20, 1913. Published originally by Constable and Co., London, 1913.

[50]These were never completely revised but after many delays were finally published after Osler's death.

[51]Revere spent most of the year 1913 with a tutor, improving his proficiency in Greek and Latin in order to pass his entrance examination to Oxford.

[52]As usual, guests had crowded the "Open Arms" for a festive Christmas (1913).

FIGURE 18. Lieutenant Edward Revere Osler at home on leave, spring 1917. (From Cushing papers in Osler Library at McGill University.)

# XIII

## The War Years

*Fear at my heart, as at a cup, my lifeblood seemed to sip.\**

There was never a lovelier summer in England than that of 1914. In Oxford flowers bloomed with rainbow gloriousness in the beautiful college parks. In the towns and villages, brightly colored geraniums and spring flowers filled numerous window boxes. Happy voices were heard throughout the land. In London the social season was at its gayest, with gallant young Englishmen and radiant debutantes rushing from ball to ball.

The surface of English life reflected only the pageantry and serenity of Britain's wonderful century of unchallenged prestige and security; an era that was rapidly passing, for war clouds were gathering over Europe. But in England no one could anticipate or imagine the holocaust that was about to engulf them.

The Oslers were busy planning their "annual" trip to America. His letters of this period give no hint of anxiety concerning the uncertainty that existed over the international situation. In the average English home war was considered hardly possible.

The declaration of war by Austria on the little country of Serbia set off a tragic chain of events. When Russia ordered mobilization on July 31, 1914, Germany reacted by declaring war against Russia. England was trying desperately to stem the tide, but on August 3, 1914, German troops invaded Belgium, unleashing terrific destruction and havoc on an unsuspecting world. Because of her treaty obligations to Belgium, England was forced to enter the war — first issuing an ultimatum and then declaring war on Germany on August 4, 1914.

---

\*Samuel Taylor Coleridge, "The Ancient Mariner."

4th [September, 1914]
13, Norham Gardens,
Oxford.

Dear Ned,[1]

I was to have sailed tomorrow, but of course I cannot leave with
the wretched war raging.[2] We shall come out on top in the long run.
How splendidly Canada is doing[.] Grace & the boy sailed on the 30
of July but returned by the same steamer[.][3]

Love to all
Yours. ever
W.O.

England was woefully unprepared for war, but the call to arms
awakened a fervent patriotic spirit throughout the island, and the
Commonwealth. The Oslers immediately entered into the country's preparation for war. It was Sir William's belief that war never
settled anything, but he was far from a pacifist. His wife, with
typical New England efficiency, organized the ladies in Oxford
for the purpose of supplying the soldiers with "extras." Throughout the war both worked unceasingly to alleviate human suffering
and to promote victory for England. Osler was appointed an
honorary colonel in the British Territorial Army. He served as
consultant to several army hospitals, including the Canadian Army
Hospital at Taplow. In addition, his advice and services were frequently sought by the War Office in London.

Canada's immediate rally to England's aid caused Osler un-
concealed pride. In a sense he felt the members of the Canadian
Army to be his personal wards.

From the Regius Professor of Medicine, Oxford.

9, October, 1914.

Dear Ned,

Sorry to hear you have been laid up. It is not often that you are
'knocked out.'

---

[1]Quoted by Cushing, vol. II, p. 430.

[2]Osler had booked passage for America on the *Aquitania* for September 5, 1914.

[3]Mrs. Osler and Revere sailed on the *R.H.S. Calgarian* on July 31, 1914. It was
while they were enroute that England declared war on Germany. After a short
hastily arranged visit with family and friends in Canada, they returned to England
on the same boat.

We are all very hard at work here. Expecting the Canadians this week.[4] I do not know when I shall be out, but certainly not until after the war.[5]

I enclose you a little address which I gave to the soldiers in one of the camps.[6]

Sincerely yours,
Wm Osler

The Oslers had another problem beside that of relief for the sick and homeless. Revere was nearing military age, and with the ever-mounting casuality lists arriving daily from France, "fear was at their hearts."

Revere entered Christ Church College on October 9, 1914. This was the day for which the Oslers had worked and prayed. However, with war raging, most of the young men were volunteering for the army. Revere was deeply patriotic and wished to join the army, but said "I will do what Dad thinks best and train here this term." He was, however, to reveal his makeup as a man and a patriot in the fast-fading years of his young life.

Revere did not do very well in military training during his first year at Oxford. Possibly his heart was not in it, and he was not recommended for a commission. This, then, presented the Oslers with a dilemma. Revere was now of military age and with no commission, the only alternative left him was to enlist in the British Army.

From the Regius Professor of Medicine, Oxford.

5, January, 1915.

Dear Ned,

So glad to hear that O'Connor thinks your eyes are better.

[4]The Canadian Expeditionary Forces arrived in England in November 1914. It would seem they all had letters of introduction to the Oslers, as the "Open Arms" was soon crowded with members of the Canadian army on leave.

[5]Osler was never to return to his native Canada.

[6]There was no compulsory vaccination in the British army. In fact, there was great opposition on the part of the antivivisectionist and antivaccinationists to any compulsory legislation of this nature. Therefore, it was necessary to appeal directly to the newly enlisted men. Osler had many "heart-to-heart" talks with the men in camp. One of these was entitled "Bacilli and Bullets" which was issued by the Oxford Press in 1914 as a penny war pamphlet and was widely circulated. It is possible that this is the address he sent Milburn.

We had a busy Christmas — two or three of the fellows from the Contingent on Salisbury Plain, where they are in a sea of mud.[7] The weather has been most unfortunate. We have never had so much rain. The whole country is soaked. Things are looking brighter here, and it is a great matter that at the beginning of the sixth month Germany has not even finished with Belgium. But it is a devil of a mess! Revere has been in the Training Corps here, and is now joining the Universities and Public Schools Regiment.

Love to Mrs. Milburn and the girls.

Sincerely yours,<br>Wm Osler

Osler was able to obtain an appointment for Revere as Assistant Commissary Officer of the McGill Hospital Unit, and he served with them, both in England and France.

From the Regius Professor of Medicine, Oxford.

5, May, 1915.

Dear Ned,[8]

Sorry to hear that you have had more trouble with your eyes and still more with your ears. I am afraid that it is a type associated with age and the hardening of the tissues in the ear, which is very difficult to help by any apparatus. On this you might safely take O'Conner's opinion, as I have heard of him as a very good man.

We are very busy. I am connected with three or four hospitals and have to be away a great deal, but the work is most interesting. The Canadians have covered themselves with glory, and everybody is talking about their bravery. We are getting back a lot of wounded, among them my sister's son, Campbell Gwyn, who has a bullet in his arm.[9] Revere is joining the McGill unit as Colonel Birkett's orderly officer.[10] He has been for nearly three months at Cleveden [Cliveden], where he has picked up a good deal about his duties. We are expecting the McGill people over at any time. I think they will take charge of a large hospital somewhere in France.

Love to Mrs. Milburn and the girls.<br>Sincerely yours,<br>Wm Osler.

---

[7]The Canadian Expeditionary Forces were encamped on the Salisbury Plain.

[8]Quoted by Cushing, vol. II, p. 475.

[9]Campbell Gwyn was Osler's sister Chattie's son.

[10]Revere originally trained for his work with the McGill Hospital Unit at the Canadian Hospital at Taplow near the Astor Estate at Clivedon. He later joined the Unit at Shorncliffe.

The "Open Arms" was a refuge for Canadian relatives on leave, medical officers from McGill, and later, when the United States entered the war, for onetime students from Philadelphia and Baltimore. The house at 13 Norham Gardens, Oxford, was continually filled. Osler was a generous host, and his entertainment of his guests was always delightful. His conversation has been described as "without effort or show," but his vast knowledge and the depth of his wisdom could be clearly discerned.

His letters to Milburn during this period were short notes. Usually typewritten, they contained a few hopeful words about the war, brief mention of his son; and then he would abruptly initiate a new subject. Military operations did not interest him, and he rarely, if ever, mentioned them in his letters, although he never wavered in expressing his belief in ultimate victory. Throughout the war years, his letters ever reflected his anxiety over the safety of his son.

> 10th [December 1915]
> 13, Norham Gardens,
> Oxford.
>
> Dear Ned
> Please hand the enclosed to Mrs Milburn to spend in the family for Xmas[.][11] I hope you are all well & will have a happy gathering. It will be a sad Xmas in many families. Many of my friends here have lost their boys; it is a terrible tragedy. Revere is joining the Field Ambulance as he is tired of the inaction in the Hospital life.[12] He has been near Boulogne for 7 months with the McGill men.[13] I am very busy — hospital work & all sorts of odds and ends to do[.] I send you a couple of addresses which may be of interest. The country is full of Canadians — a fine lot too[.]
> Love to you all
> Yours-ever,
> Wm Osler

Revere's patriotic conscience could not find rest in his present duties and caused him continued dissatisfaction in his relatively

---

[11]The customary Christmas check for the Milburn family was enclosed.

[12]In order to get into the more active combat zone, it was Revere's intention to join the Field Ambulance Unit.

[13]The McGill Hospital Unit was at Etaples, France. Osler had visited his son there in September 1915.

safe position in the McGill Unit. He believed he should be serving with his contemporaries in the fighting zone. He had accepted the position with the McGill Hospital Unit in acquiescence to the wishes of his father. Revere's deep sense of duty finally convinced his parents that they must accept his wishes for combat duty. In February 1916 he transferred to the British Army.

Revere had a short leave home in late 1915 before entering training for the British Army Artillery Corps at Newcastle. The Oslers found that he had matured considerably, and to his father's great delight, Revere now enjoyed discussing books and scholars. This accomplishment was indeed the fruit of much effort and patience on Osler's part. In the last few years of his life, Revere had become an increasingly interested bibliophile and had started a collection of rare books printed during the Elizabethan Age. After Revere's death his parents founded the "Tudor and Stuart Club" at Johns Hopkins University as a memorial to their son "in grateful recognition of the happy years we spent in Baltimore." Revere's collection of rare books was to serve as a nucleus for a library of the club and an Edward Revere Osler Memorial Fund was established to perpetuate and expand this collection. The purpose of the club was to encourage the study of English literature of the Tudor and Stuart periods. The club is still active, and the fund is used "for the further purchase of books relating to these periods, and the promotion of good fellowship and a love of literature among its members."[14]

In July 1916 Osler visited his son at Newcastle. They had a wonderfully happy weekend visiting in the Durham Cathedral and its adjoining library.

Post Card:

[March] 26th. [1916]

Sorry to hear you have not been well.[15] Send word how you are from time to time

All well here. Boy in good form.

Love to you all

Wm Osler

---

[14]Keys, T. E.: Edward Revere Osler, 1895-1917, *Arch Intern Med* (Chicago), *114:* 284-293, Aug. 1964.

Post Card:

4th [1916]

Excuse a p.c. but I am hard pressed with work. Ralph was a fine lad — and of great promise.[16] Revere is in camp at Newcastle getting training in the RF. artillery.

Not very likely to involve the other side in case you refer to.[17]

Love to you all

W.O.

Soon after Revere finished with the Royal Artillery training, he was sent to France. He seemed relieved and happy to be finally in the fighting zone. Certainly a part of this cheerfulness was for home consumption and to boost the sagging morale of his beloved "Muz and Dad." Osler's anxiety for his son's safety was countervailed somewhat by his increasing work load. He was fortunate too in that he had his library to turn to as a refuge — "for books have a timeless quality." In his letters of this period, he often quoted Dante "the seen arrow slackens its flight" and added "we are steeling our hearts for anything that may happen."[18]

24th [November 1916]
13, Norham Gardens,
Oxford.

Dear Ned

Please hand the enclosed to Mrs. Milburn to spend on you & the girls for Xmas.[19] All well here. Revere in the thick of this Ancre push. He joined his Battery about 2 mos ago in France & likes the work.[20] Of course we are very anxious, but it is the right thing for the boy to do & we should not be happy if he was not in it. I am very busy —

[15]For the past several years it had been evident that Milburn was not in good health and Osler showed his concern in his letters to Ned.

[16]Frank Osler's son, Ralph, was killed in action in France in June 1916. He had visited Oxford only a month before he was killed.

[17]This is possibly in reference to Ned's difficulty with his ear.

[18]Cushing.

[19]Again at Christmas Osler sent his usual check to "hand to Mrs. Milburn." One daughter of Milburn stated that she still remembered this regular Christmas gift. This custom was continued throughout his life.

[20]Revere was a lieutenant in the British Army Artillery and was sent to France October 17, 1916, directly into the heavy fighting along the Somme River.

away a great deal. We are all glad to have the Can. Army Medical business settled.[21] Sam was an impossible creature.

I hope you are keeping pretty well.

Love to you all

Your affec friend

Wm Osler

Christmas at the "Open Arms" in 1916 was as busy as ever, but there was an emptiness with Revere away at the battle front.

In the late spring of 1917, Revere had a ten-day leave at home. It was to be his last, and he spent most of the time doing what he loved most, fishing. There was also time to attend book auctions with his father, much to the latter's delight.

>                                    25th 17 [April 1917]
>                                    13, Norham Gardens,
>                                    Oxford.

Dear Ned

I have just written scolding N.[22] for not letting me know she was in London[.] She has now gone to Brighton — I suppose to the big new Hospital. She should have come to us direct. I must have missed one of your letters. You said you would notify me of her sailing[.] I have yours of the 27th ult. today [25th]. She will be very happy and must come to us whenever she can. I have written to the chief matron about her[.] Revere has been for six weeks in the thick of this fighting — the battery never more than a few days in one place. He writes most cheerfully but we have had anxious spells of 12-14 days without a letter[.] He had hoped for leave March 1st & then this retreat upset everything & his brigade has been following up ever since. My sister

---

[21]In the summer of 1916, a controversy arose over alleged mistreatment of Canadian soldiers confined in British hospitals. Osler, as consultant to the Canadian Army Medical Corps in England, felt that the charges were without basis. Nevertheless, a Board of Inquiry was appointed, and the Surgeon-General of the Canadian Army Medical Corps was recalled because of purported findings. Osler, who felt that there was little to justify such an accusation, was incensed at this injustice and threatened to resign. Later, the Canadian Minister of Militia, who seems to have precipitated this furor, was removed from office, and his successor appointed another commission (on which Osler was asked to serve, but he declined). However, when this commission repudiated the report of the original Board of Inquiry, the Surgeon-General was reinstated, and Osler's resignation as consultant to the Canadian Army Medical Corps withdrawn.

[22]Nonie Milburn, Ned's daughter, was a trained nurse serving with the Canadian Army.

lost a splendid boy at Vimy ridge.[23] Sorry to hear you have been knocked up. I am all right again and very busy.
Love to you all

Yours, ever      Wm Osler

On August 29, 1917, Revere was severely wounded. He is quoted as saying to the first officer who bent over him, "This will take me home," words fraught with more meaning than he thought. Several of William Osler's former American students, including Drs. Harvey Cushing and George Crile, were able to come to his aid; but, in spite of dramatic efforts on their part to save his life, Revere died the next day.

"On September 1, 1917, somewhere in Flander's Field [Plot 4, Row F], wrapped in an army blanket, covered by a weather-worn Union Jack, the great-great grandson of Paul Revere was buried."[24] Major Davidson, Revere's commanding officer, wrote, never knowing that Sir William Osler would see the note: "Osler [Revere] was the personification of purity, unsordidness and unselfishness. It is the killing of such a boy that makes me loathe war."[25] Revere had written his parents "I have no regrets except for my own shortcomings, only endless love and gratitude for you both." He had been the indispensable ingredient in Osler's happiness; a gentle blue-eyed boy and a passionate fisherman. Though an indifferent student, he was in the words of Osler: "everything that a father could wish, a dear, good laddie,"[26] and "a sweeter laddie never lived."

2. IX. 17<br>13, Norham Gardens,<br>Oxford.

Dear Ned[27]

Thanks for your cable. The blow is a hard one but we must face it bravely He was such a dear laddie, always so loving & considerate &

---

[23]Major Campbell Gwyn, Canadian Infantry, killed in action April 9, 1917.

[24]Cushing, vol. II, p. 577.

[25]Reid, Edith (Gittings): *The Great Physician, a Short Life of Sir William Osler.* New York, Oxford U. P., 1931.

[26]Cushing, vol. II, p. 550, from the letter Sir William wrote to his beloved Revere on his 21st birthday.

[27]This was a letter in reply to a cable of condolence from Ned after he learned that Revere had been killed in action. Even in his deep grief Osler was able to think of small kindnesses he could do for his friend.

had developed into a fine character. We had so much in common so that the parting is a terrible wrench. We have no details.

I hope you have a good news of Nonie. I have told her to come to us for her first leave.

Love to you all

> Your affec friend
> Wm Osler

The seen arrow had "slackened its flight." Osler took the death of Revere bravely, and as one would expect, tried to spare others, especially his wife, the bitter grief over their loss; his staunch wife made efforts to soften Osler's loss, trying to forget her own. He buried himself in his work, driving himself beyond the limit of his physical endurance, which unquestionably contributed to the undermining of his health.

He mentioned Revere's death only briefly in letters to his friends. Possibly it was such a common story in England in the trying days of 1917 that each silently bore his own grief. His letter to Milburn, dated September 2, 1917, reflects his reluctance to burden his friends with his grief. He merely mentions Revere's death in passing. He must have known Milburn would understand how he felt, as Milburn had also lost his only son.

Osler at no time evinced any animosity toward the Germans for his loss, and he allowed no one in his presence to do so.

> 18 April, 1918.

From the Regius Professor of Medicine, Oxford.

Dear Ned,

Sorry to hear you have been laid up. Nonie writes that she is quite well again and at work at Buckston! She seems a very capable woman, and full of good sense.

> Love to you all
> Wm. Osler

**Post Card:**

> 30-XI-18

Photo excellent — except for the frost on top it might be N.M in *70* instead of N M at 70[.]

Xmas wishes to you all

> Yours
> W.O.

FIGURE 19. E. F. Milburn in later life. (Courtesy of Miss Ruby Milburn.)

# XIV

# The Journey's End

*The harbour is nearly reached — such delightful companions all the way**

The year 1919 was an eventful time for Osler. He was kept busy by many things — campaigns, speaking engagements, and his ever swelling correspondence. But overwork, advancing age, and the heavy shadow of his silent grief had taken their toll. He was most certainly driving himself far more than his health could endure, but work left little time for the feeling of continual loneliness he felt for his son. Osler, in spite of his emaciated body, always managed to present a good front and outwardly appeared to be in cheerful spirits. However, Lady Osler wrote that he was pathetic and that it was surprising that his attempts at "keeping up" did not kill him.

The war was over at long last, and the medical officers were on their way home. Osler organized dinners and receptions honoring hospital units in which he had many friends. Frequently, the "Open Arms" was filled to capacity with guests and friends who were on their way back to America and wished to say goodbye. There was much coming and going, and all were welcomed warmly and fed with the best that postwar England could afford.

Osler's humaneness was reflected in his persistent and eventually successful efforts to alleviate the hunger of children in postwar Austria. He organized a campaign to send food to these unfortunate children through his friend Professor Weinckbach[1] of

---

*Quotation from a letter of Osler to Mrs. Brewster, New York City, dated November 23, 1919, quoted in Keyes, T. E.: Edward Revere Osler, *Arch Intern* (Chicago), *114*, 1964.

[1]Professor Karl Friedrich Weinckbach was an eminent cardiologist of Vienna, Austria.

Vienna, even though this plan was met with open hostility from many of the people of Oxford. The heartache and bitterness of the war were still too fresh in everyone's mind and it would be many years before this feeling would be assuaged.

His wonderful library occupied a constant undercurrent in his thoughts. He had by now compiled a veritable treasure in masterpieces of the world's medical literature, which he had decided to give to McGill University in his native Canada. The cataloging had been underway for several years, but was not finished in his lifetime.

Lady Osler on several occasions intervened to prevent his becoming involved in further professional activities for undoubtedly she saw the terrible strain on him and felt that his strength was considerably overtaxed. Nevertheless, he gradually increased his correspondence, possibly in response to a foreboding for the future, since there was so much to which he must attend. As the end approached his pace seemed to quicken with that feeling so perfectly expressed by Robert Frost, "but I have promises to keep, and miles to go before I sleep."

He was elected president of the Classical Association in England, a most distinctive honor. His presidential address entitled "The Old Humanities and the New Science" has often been referred to as the highlight of his inspired literary efforts. He entered into its preparation with his customary enthusiasm and energy and drew on the wealth of material which he had accumulated over the years. Professor W. H. Welch of Johns Hopkins was present in the audience when Osler delivered the address and gave as his opinion, "That was Osler at his very best." Osler received widespread accolades for this essay.

His 70th birthday in July 1919 brought forth worldwide expressions of respect, affection, and remembrance. Several journals in the United States, Canada, and England issued special "Osler numbers." Unfortunately, some of the issues were so delayed in printing that Osler was on his deathbed when they arrived and never had the opportunity to read them.

The stage was now set for tragedy. Osler had been subject to bronchitis since childhood and periodically during his life was confined to the bed with complications of this condition. During the War he had several attacks of bronchial pneumonia, the last one in July 1919, which left him further weakened.

In September he made a trip to Glasgow and Edinburgh, combining a professional visit with some business of the University Grants Committee. On leaving Edinburgh he was confronted with a national railway strike and in order to return home had to secure an automobile at Newcastle. Unfortunately, he had to spend the night on the way and during the trip caught a cold. Once at home he was immediately confined to the bed with a severe attack of acute bronchitis.

This bout of illness was unusually protracted, and gradually he realized that this was no ordinary attack. Throughout October and November his illness showed intermittent fluctuations in its course, which often gave hope to him and his wife. However, the appearance of a friction rub and continued cough and fever heralded serious complications. The isolation of the influenza bacillus from the pleural fluid brought a quiet resignation to the inevitable, for he now realized that he was suffering from a critical infection. Nevertheless, a valiant fight was initiated in an attempt to save his life. Consultants were summoned from London, but in spite of every effort, his cough and fever persisted. Throughout this period Osler was fully aware of the gravity of his malady and did not attempt to conceal this from his wife.

Even during such serious illness Osler's ever present humor was demonstrated by an incident that occurred during one of the visits of the London physicians.[1] A specimen of urine was requested in the course of the examination. Somehow, in spite of his weakened condition, Osler managed to obtain some fine gravel which he prankishly added to the specimen. He became the happy mischievous boy once again when the specialists gathered around his bed and gravely informed him that in addition to his lung disease his kidneys were in a "deplorable condition."

---

[1]Quoted in Cushing.

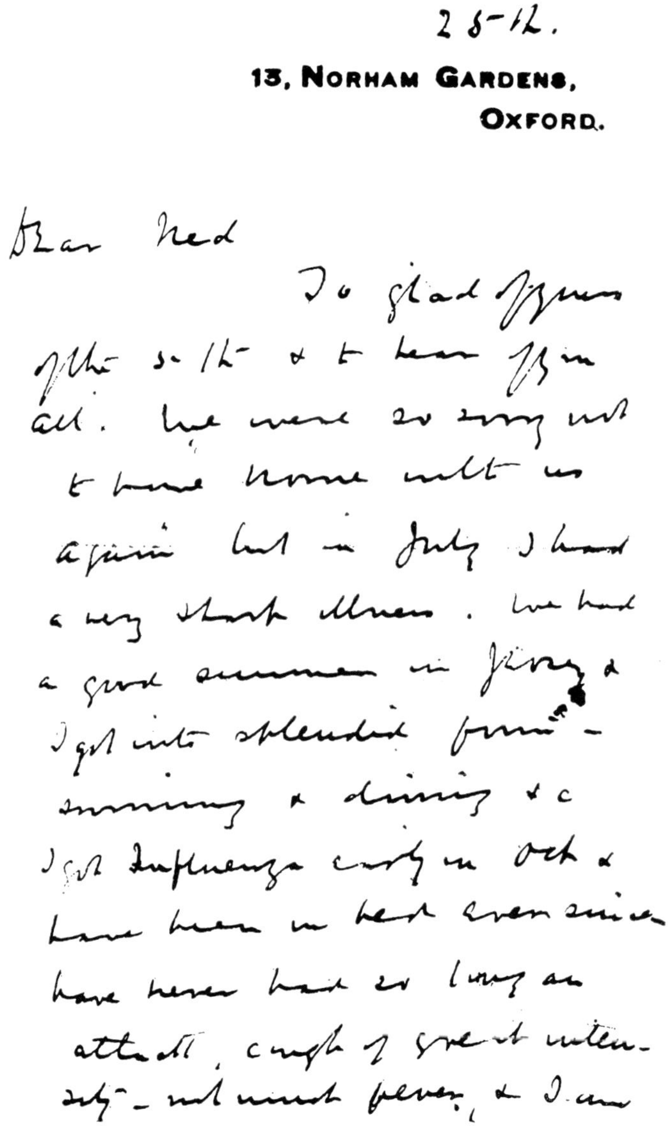
25-12.

13, NORHAM GARDENS,
OXFORD.

Dear Ned

So glad to get news of the sick & to hear of you all. We were so sorry not to have Norman with us again but in July I had a very short illness. We had a good summer in Jersey & I got into splendid form — swimming & diving &c. I got Influenza early in Oct & have been in bed ever since. have never had so long an attack, cough of great intensity — not much fever, & I am

FIGURE 20. Osler's last letter to Ned Milburn, written November 1919 during Osler's final illness. It was dated Christmas Day. From the Reynolds Historical Library in the University of Alabama in Birmingham, Medical Center.

bad & will a learned name!
but I 'spect to pull thro'!
So glad you liked the address.
The "mealy mouthed mid-
Victorian" was used in —
general sense. I am sending
a copy of letter for. Am. M. ass.
which has a good picture of me.
The memorial v ts. for my
70th birthday are not yet ready.
They were presented in dummy
form on the 12th at the Royal
Soc. med. Sunday, — a most
interesting occasion.
Love to you all. Please give
enclosed to Mrs Mill——

Yours ever.

W.O.

**13, NORHAM GARDENS,**
**OXFORD.**

*Please spend this*
*on anything for*
*dear Ned. with my*
*Xmas love.*

25-12
13, Norham Gardens,
Oxford.

Dear Ned[2]

So glad of yours of the 5th & to hear of you all. We were so sorry not to have Nonie with us again[,] but in July I had a very short illness. We had a good summer in Jersey & I got into splendid form — swimming and diving &c[.] I got influenza early in Oct & have been in bed ever since — have never had so long an attack, cough of great intensity — not much fever, & I am not out of the woods yet. — In bed & with a trained nurse! but I 'spect to pull thro! So glad you liked the address[.][3] The "mealy mouthed Mid-Victorian" was used in a generic sense. I am sending a copy of the Jr. Am. M. Ass. which has a good picture of me.[4] The memorial vols. for my 70th birthday are not yet ready. They were presented in dummy form on the 12th at the

---

[2]"Osler's last letter to me." (Ned Milburn's notation.) This last letter brought to a close more than a half century of correspondence from Osler to Milburn. Although dated Christmas 1919, he wrote it in late November of that year. He was critically ill by Christmas.

[3]Reference is made here to his address to the Classical Association entitled "The Old Humanities and the New Science," a copy of which he certainly must have sent Milburn as he had unfailingly done with all his speeches.

[4]An editorial entitled "Sir William Osler at Seventy — A Retrospect," together with his picture, appeared in the *JAMA, 73* (No. 2), July 12, 1919.

Royal Soc. Med. London. — a most interesting occasion.[5]
Love to you all. Please give enclosed to Mrs Milburn[6]
Yours ever,
W.O.
[Note enclosed] Please spend this on anything for dear Ned. with my
Xmas love.[7]


This is the last letter that Milburn received from Osler. In Milburn's letter to Cushing, after Osler's death, he wrote, "The last letter I received from him was written in the last week of November, 1919, and was received by me two or three days before Christmas."

During the last few November days, he became too ill to write letters. He would often scribble notes on scraps of paper that were later collected and filed away. One of his last letters was to Mrs. Brewster, a friend in New York City, written on November 23, 1919, in which he said, "The harbour is nearly reached — such delightful companions all the way — and my Isaac waiting for me, already there and perhaps his old friend, Isaac [Walton] and some other fishermen."

Empyema was identified and aspiration undertaken, but with little improvement. Later a thoracotomy was performed, and finally, a lung abscess was diagnosed. The course of his illness quickened; the end was near. Mrs. Osler's sister, Mrs. Chapin, and Osler's nephew, Dr. W. W. Francis, came to Norham Gardens. On the afternoon of December 29, 1919, William Osler died quietly at 4:30 after a severe hemorrhage from the operative wound.

---

[5]The Birthday Memorial Volumes entitled "Contributions to Medical and Biological Research: Dedicated to Sir William Osler in Honour of His Seventieth Birthday, July 12, 1919, by His Pupils and Co-Workers" under editorship of C. L. Davis, were presented in dummy form at the Royal Society of Medicine, London. Sir Clifford Allbritt presided and Osler responded with a prepared speech. Osler took sick at this meeting and was confined to bed with a fever and cold. The actual finished volumes did not reach Oxford until December 27, 1919, when Osler was too ill to see them. See Cushing, vol. 11, p. 659.
[6]The usual Christmas check was enclosed.
[7]This note was in all probability attached to the enclosed check. So, even to his last letter he continued in the thoughtful acts of kindness which characterized the friendship between Osler and Milburn.

"So passed into history, untimely, even though he had attained unto the allotted span, the greatest physician in history."[8]

Craigleigh,<br>
Rosedale.<br>
12 Jan. 1920

Dear Mr. Milburn,[9]

Thank you very much for your message of sympathy[.] The death of Wm Osler is a loss to all & a personal grief to all who have known him

Yours sincerely<br>
Edmund Osler

---

[8]Adami, J. G.: *Osler Memorial Number,* Bull. No. IX, Inter. ass. of Med Museums, Abbott, M. E., (Ed.), Montreal, 1927.

[9]This note from Osler's brother, Sir Edmund Boyd Osler, was sent from his home "Craigleigh," in Toronto, apparently in reply to a message of sympathy from Milburn after the death of William Osler.

FIGURE 21. The Osler Library in the McIntyre Medical Sciences Building at McGill University. (Chris F. Payne - Photo Service, Montreal.)

# Epilogue

*I am a part of all that I have met*\*

It was New Year's Day, 1920, and in the waning light of a mid-winter's day, the great, near great, and ordinary people, men representing all that he had loved, came to pay their last respects to the greatly beloved William Osler. The funeral service was held in Christ Church Cathedral, Oxford. The lovely old church, mellowed by time and memory, was filled to overflowing. The service was brief and simple, and it ended as he wanted, with the strains of Peter Aberlard's "O Quanta Qualia," "O what the joy and the glory must be." They left him that New Year's night in the Lady Watching Chamber near the quaint effigy which surmounts the tomb of Robert Burton, whose works Osler had so admired.

The next day a sad little group accompanied Osler's remains to London where he was cremated. Lady Osler, Mrs. Chapin (Osler's sister), Dr. W. W. Francis (his nephew), and his brother, Frank,[1] were present at the private Commital Service at Golder's Green in London.

It was Osler's wish that his library should go to McGill University, but he was anxious that the catalogue should be finished before the books were sent. He had said this would still require "ten years of not too senile leisure." To the accomplishment of this wish Lady Osler devoted the remainder of her life encouraging the editors, financing the cataloging, and finally establishing a fund of £10,000 for the maintenance of the library. She died in 1928, when the work was almost done and the first books packed for shipment. Her death seemed a timely requital for she had

---

\*Osler, in his second edition of *Aequanimitas and Other Addresses,* quoted Tennyson's "Ulysses."

[1]Frank Osler was the last of the Osler brothers to survive. He died in London in 1933.

119

dreaded the day when the library would be gone, as with it would go some simulance of continuity with the past.

His library at McGill University is in a beautiful room in the McIntyre Medical Sciences Building. At the end of the room in the center of an alcove is the Vernon bronze medallion bearing his portrait, behind which repose his and Lady Osler's ashes.

Osler had written

> I like to think of my books in an alcove of a fireproof library in some institution that I love: at the back of the alcove, an open fireplace and a few easy chairs, and on the mantelpiece an urn with my ashes, through which my astral self could peek at the books I have loved, and enjoy the delight with which kindred souls still in the flesh would handle them.

It is now more than two score years since Osler died, but his influence lives on. One of the first physicians he trained at Hopkins, Dr. W. S. Thayer, has succinctly and accurately summed up his life story with these words

> He was a keen observer, a brilliant clinician. His contributions to medicine and medical education were important. He was a great teacher. But his main strength lay in the singular and unique charm of his presence, in the sparkling brilliancy of his mind, in the rare beauty of his character and of his life, and in the examples that he set to his fellows and to his students.[2]

We cannot leave this summation, however, without acknowledging the heritage William Osler left us in the art of true friendship. He literally poured out his life in acts of kindness, concern, and interest to friends whose names were legion. It is the hope of the writer that the letters in this volume from William Osler to Ned Milburn will give the reader some idea of the depth and continuation of that friendship which began in boyhood and lasted until death separated them. It can be truly said that if anyone knew how to be a friend, William Osler did. Not only was he a "part of all those whom he had met" but he became a part of the lives of all who met him, and his influence for all that is noble and good in this world continues still.

---

[2]*Osler Memorial Number*, Bull. No. IX, Inter. Ass. of Med Museums, Abbott, M. E., (Ed., Montreal, 1927, p. 295.

# Sources of Material

In addition to the letters published in this volume, I have relied heavily on Harvey Cushing's monumental *Life of Sir William Osler,* published in 1924. Without this immense and painstaking compilation it would have been difficult, if not impossible, to prepare this manuscript. Cushing had access to a portion of the letters used in this manuscript and used some of them in his text, though frequently with different emphasis and context.

The Osler Library at McGill University has made available a large amount of Osler memorabilia, mostly previously published photographs and notes. Also, the Cushing Library at Yale University Medical School has provided us with facsimiles of the correspondence between Dr. Harvey Cushing and Ned Milburn during the time when Cushing was compiling the Osler Biography.

Information was also gained from the *Trinity College School Record,* F. J. Wainwright, editor, Port Hope, Ontario, 1915. Bean, B. R. and Bean, W. B.: *Sir William Osler, Aphorisms,* Springfield, Thomas, 1961, helped to see Osler through the eyes of a student.

I found of value the small volume privately printed by Arnold Muirhead on the life of Lady Osler. It provided excellent information on the period after Osler's death and details of the cataloging and transfer of the Osler Library to McGill.

The University of Toronto generously allowed the perusal of a privately printed volume entitled, *Records of the Lives of Ellen Free Pickton and Featherstone Lake Osler,* Oxford U. P., 1915.

The Bulletin (No. IX) of the International Association of Medical Museums; the *Sir William Osler Memorial Number,* edited by M. E. Abbott, 1927, has furnished much illumination or Sir William's activities during each period of his life. Anne Wilkinson's *Lions in the Way* Toronto, Macmillian 1956, was an invaluable source of information on Osler's early life as well as that of the Osler family, both in Canada and England.

# Author's Note

In researching and writing about the life and character of a man, it is impossible not to become caught and bound up in his actions, personality, and revelations of the many aspects which contribute to the totality of a person. I confess that as I have written, I too, as many others before me, have fallen captive to this gentle though forceful, simple though brilliant, serious yet gay person — this noble man Osler, one of "the choice and master spirits of the age."

# Index